Connect to
NCTM Standards 2000

Making the Standards
Work at Grade 7

Francis (Skip) Fennell, Ph.D.

Honi J. Bamberger, Ph.D.

Thomas E. Rowan, Ph.D.

Kay B. Sammons

Anna R. Suarez

Creative Publications
A Tribune Education Company

Acknowledgments

Project Editors → Diane Nieker, Jeff Stiegel

Writers → Tim Burnett, Marilyn Davis, Beth Sycamore

Writing and Editorial Services → MathLink, Inc.

Design Director → Karen Stack

Design → Gerta Sorensen-London

Project Coordinator → Barbara Quincer

Cover Illustration → Jim Dandy

Illustrators → Susan Aiello, Jim Dandy, Sarah Frederking

Production → Inkwell Publishing Solutions, Inc.

Manufacturing → Dallas Richards

© 2000 Creative Publications®, Inc.
Two Prudential Plaza
Chicago, IL 60601

This is an independent publication and is not affiliated with, or sponsored by, the NCTM. The NCTM 2000 Standards are not reproduced in this book. This book is designed to be read independently of the *Principles and Standards for School Mathematics* and to aid educators in preparing to teach in a manner consistent with the *Principles and Standards*.

ISBN 0-7622-1249-7
Catalog No. 21708
Customer Service 800-624-0822
http://www.creativepublications.com
1 2 3 4 5 6 7 8 MAL 05 04 03 02 01 00

Contents

Introduction   iv

About the Standards   2

Standard 1: Number and Operation   16

Standards-Based Lessons

Multiplying Fractions   18

Recognizing Proportion Problems   24

Exploring Percents   30

Revised Textbook Lesson   Understanding Integers   36

Standard 2: Algebra   42

Standards-Based Lessons   Simplifying Expressions   44

Using Equations   50

Analyzing Patterns   56

Revised Textbook Lesson   Translating Algebraic Expressions   62

Standard 3: Geometry   68

Standards-Based Lessons   Exploring Transformations   70

Representing Views of Three-Dimensional Shapes   76

Analyzing Transformations and Congruence   82

Revised Textbook Lesson   Investigating Angle-Sum Relationships   88

Standard 4: Measurement   94

Standards-Based Lessons   Investigating Unit Rates   96

Relating Area and Perimeter   102

Exploring Surface Area and Volume   108

Revised Textbook Lesson   Investigating Volume of Pyramids and Cones   114

Standard 5: Data Analysis and Probability   120

Standards-Based Lessons   Using Measures of Central Tendency   122

Interpreting Graphs   128

Investigating Probability   134

Revised Textbook Lesson   Reading and Interpreting Circle Graphs   140

Create Your Own Lesson

Understanding Exponents   146

Overview

Since *Curriculum and Evaluation Standards for School Mathematics* was released in 1989, much has been learned about how ideas work in the classroom and how students learn mathematics. The release of the *Principles and Standards for School Mathmatics* creates an opportunity for us to examine our goals, our math curricula, and our teaching methods in light of these new insights and to consider practices and procedures that will improve school mathematics education. As did the original draft, *Principles and Standards* promotes ways for all educators to strengthen the teaching and learning of mathematics by addressing two important concerns: the characteristics of instructional programs that will provide high-quality mathematical experiences for students as they progress through school, and the mathematical content and processes students should know and use as they advance from grade to grade.

General Overview

Connect to NCTM Standards 2000 is designed to help you understand and implement the NCTM standards. Regardless of your teaching style, the information presented in this book will help you to make the standards work. *Principles and Standards* identifies ten standards. Five of those standards are described as content standards that organize all of mathematics into five broad areas of learning; they address *what* students learn. The other five standards, the process standards, are concerned with *how* students learn and how information is presented.

Today, more than ever, there is a need for all students to have a strong base in mathematics. This means that students do not just memorize facts and procedures, but that they have an understanding of mathematics and mathematical thinking. The interplay between content and process is complicated, but integrating the two is critical if our students are to receive the mathematics education they will need to function effectively in the world they will grow into.

The lessons contained within *Connect to NCTM Standards 2000* are organized into sections by content. Each section contains four lessons dealing with some aspect of that content standard. Each lesson demonstrates ways to develop the content by using the process standards. An overview highlights grade-level content skills and gives a brief description of the four lessons for that standard.

Content Standards

Number and Operation

Algebra

Geometry

Measurement

Data Analysis and Probability

Process Standards

Problem Solving

Reasoning and Proof

Communication

Connections

Representation

The last section of the book, entitled Create Your Own, is designed to help you develop lessons of your own that will comfortably incorporate the NCTM standards with your teaching style.

About the Lessons

Each content standard section contains four lessons that address some aspect of the content at the grade level. Three of the lessons have been specially developed to model ways the process standards can be used to develop the content being presented. The fourth lesson examines a typical math textbook lesson in terms of how the process standards are incorporated into that lesson. Suggestions are offered for increasing the focus on three of the five process standards to create a more effective lesson. Then a lesson is presented modeling how those suggestions can be implemented.

As you read through the lessons, keep in mind that what is offered is only one possible approach. You might have a completely different idea about how to develop the concept, and that's fine. These lessons are intended to provide examples of how the process standards can work to make mathematics lessons more meaningful, and, to model questions and techniques that you might incorporate into your teaching. As you read through the lessons, pay attention to how the process standards are being used. Use the ideas presented as a springboard for your own ideas.

Each lesson is intended for a single class period. Some introduce a concept, others require students have some experience with the concept, and still others are meant to be used at the end of a unit. As you examine these lessons, think about how and where they fit into your curriculum. Any of the lessons here can be used as a replacement for the comparable lesson in your current math program. Try the lessons and see the difference incorporating the process standards can make.

Creating Your Own Lessons

The last section of the book is designed to help you develop lessons of your own that incorporate the NCTM standards and are compatible with your teaching style. You will find questions to help you focus on ideas to consider as you begin to organize a standards-based lesson. You will also have an opportunity to follow the thoughts and decisions one person used in the process of developing a lesson.

About the Authors

Francis (Skip) Fennell, Ph.D.

Dr. Fennell was a member of the writing team of *Principles and Standards for School Mathematics* (NCTM, 2000). He has authored mathematics textbooks, materials for both students and teachers, and numerous articles for leading mathematics journals. Dr. Fennell has served on the Board of Directors of NCTM and as Program Officer of instructional materials and teacher enhancement within the Division of Elementary, Secondary, and Informal Education at the National Science Foundation. He has been selected as Outstanding Mathematics Educator by the Maryland Council of Teachers of Mathematics, and as Professor of the Year by both the Carnegie Foundation and Western Maryland College, where he is a professor of education.

Honi J. Bamberger, Ph.D.

Dr. Bamberger is a recognized math scholar and teacher. She has taught at both the elementary school and college levels, served as an associate research scientist and mathematics consultant for Johns Hopkins University, and contributed as a consultant and content writer for the "Numbers Alive" public television series. Dr. Bamberger has presented her research findings at mathematics conferences across the country, and has been an author for a number of mathematics textbooks. Currently, Dr. Bamberger is executive director of Insight, a consulting firm specializing in professional development in mathematics education.

Thomas E. Rowan, Ph.D.

Dr. Rowan was a member of the working group that wrote the K–4 section of the *Curriculum and Evaluation Standards for School Mathematics*. Since the Standards were first published, he has worked with many school systems to help bring about the transition to standards-based classroom mathematics instruction in grades K–8. Dr. Rowan is a frequent presenter at NCTM and author of mathematics texts and numerous articles on teaching and learning mathematics. He currently teaches at the University of Maryland where he focuses on methods of teaching elementary school mathematics.

Kay B. Sammons

Kay Sammons is currently Elementary Mathematics Supervisor for the Howard County Public Schools in Ellicott City, Maryland, where she is responsible for curriculum and staff development for elementary teachers. She is a frequent presenter at state and national mathematics conferences. In addition to serving as a reviewer for NCTM publications, she has written textbooks and teacher resource materials. Ms. Sammons was honored as Elementary Mathematics Teacher of the Year by the Maryland Council Teachers of Mathematics and as Outstanding Educator of the Year by that same organization.

Anna R. Suarez

Anna Suarez is a national consultant and program director for K–8 Mathematics at the National Science Foundation in Arlington, Virginia. Her participation in an NSF-funded research study, Cognitively Guided Instruction (C.G.I.), helped to develop teachers' knowledge of students' mathematical thinking as the basis for making instructional decisions. She has written staff development materials for both the *Investigations* curriculum and Insight.

About the Standards

*T*he *Principles and Standards for School Mathematics* are built around ten curriculum standards. Five of those standards address the mathematical content, or body of mathematical knowledge, that students should learn. These content standards prescribe *what* is to be taught in mathematics. The content standards are Number and Operation, Algebra, Geometry, Measurement, and Data Analysis and Prbability.

The other five standards are process standards. The process standards describe *how* the content is delivered. They address how students will acquire the necessary mathematical content and how that knowledge will be applied. The five process standards are identified as Problem Solving, Reasoning and Proof, Communication, Connections, and Representation.

It should be pointed out that the content standards and process standards are not separate subsets of the whole, but are intricately interrelated. How mathematics is learned is as important as what mathematics is learned. The process standards help to "frame" how the content standards are presented.

It is possible to weave the process standards into the teaching of mathematics through a variety of methods. Students can and should be presented with meaningful problems to solve and situations that require them to reason through information to find solutions. They should be asked to defend their solutions and explain their thinking. In presenting a problem to students, connections might be made to a similar problem to build on previous learning. A representative model might be used to enhance students' understanding of a concept. Continuous communication, written and oral, will provide feedback about students' understanding.

For students to become mathematically powerful, it is essential that they be able to use process skills flexibly. They need to practice applying reasoning to solve problems and proving that their solutions are correct. They need to experiment with a variety of representations and have the ability to use them in solving problems and in illustrating their thinking. They should be able to communicate their mathematical thinking and solutions to the teacher and to other students both orally or in writing. Making connections between problems within mathematics is as essential as is making mathematical connections to disciplines outside of mathematics. The importance of how these processes interrelate and work together cannot be overemphasized.

Content Standards

Number and Operation

Algebra

Geometry

Measurement

Data Analysis and Probability

Process Standards

Problem Solving

Reasoning and Proof

Communication

Connections

Representation

Middle School Problem Solving

PROBLEM SOLVING IS AT THE HEART of mathematics—it is what mathematicians do. Balance is achieved through the interrelationship of conceptual learning, basic skills, and problem solving. Students need to develop concepts with concrete representations to ensure understanding and to build a strong foundation. They need basic skills in order to apply their understandings with efficiency. But most importantly, they need good problems to solve, problems in which they can utilize their conceptual understanding and basic skills.

In its simplest form, problem solving means finding a solution when the answer is not readily apparent. Because problem solving does not always follow a uniform plan, students need to develop persistence to be able to work problems through to the end. Sometimes persistence means changing direction. *Well, we know that way doesn't work. What should we try next? Is there another way we can look at this problem?* Questions that encourage students to look for other options should be an integral part of the discussions that take place in mathematics classes.

Choosing problems that have relevance to students is an important factor in creating enthusiasm for problem solving. Often, the enthusiasm of the teacher translates into a positive disposition toward problem solving for students. If statements like, *Now that's an unusual problem. I wonder how we can find the answer,* are part of a teacher's repertoire, students get the notion that problem solving is pretty interesting stuff and they are encouraged to use their own resources to find a path to the solution.

Acquiring a variety of strategies to access for problem solving is essential to experiencing success. Having flexibility to solve problems in different ways enables students to get "unstuck" if they reach a "dead end." Students should be provided with instruction and practice in using a wide range of strategies that they can then draw upon.

When students are presented with a problem that doesn't exactly fit into the context of what they already know, they need to know how to develop strategies based on their previously learned skills and concepts.

This problem was presented to a class of seventh grade students.

> The recipe for the punch that we are serving at the dance on Friday makes
> 8 gallons. A punch glass holds $\frac{3}{4}$ cup of punch. Will 8 gallons be enough to
> serve all 75 of the students expected to attend the dance? If not, how much
> more punch will be needed? Work with your group and show your work on
> paper. Be prepared to present your solution to the class.

This is a real-world problem that is relevant to students. The wonderful thing
is that like most real mathematics problems encountered outside of the
classroom, it's a messy problem.

First, students need some information they're not given. Will some students
want more than one serving punch? How many students will decline the
punch? How many servings at $\frac{3}{4}$ cup each are there in 8 gallons? Second,
students will need to decide how and where they can get the information
they need. Third, since there is really no precise answer to a problem like
this, students will need to use their estimation and reasoning skills.

Each group might approach this problem a little differently. Some will
immediately pick up a calculator and start figuring; others might start with a
visual representation. In the process of solving the problem, students might
approach the head of the dance committee to see how many tickets have been

sold, or they might canvass their friends as to their preference for punch. They might consult a standards measure table to find equivalent measures for cups, pints, quarts, and gallons.

When the task has been completed, each group should have an opportunity to present and defends its solution. A wide range of approaches and solutions will emerge. These different strategies should be compared noting similarities and differences. Students should also be asked to consider which solutions they think work best for the particular problem and why. This opens the door to a rich discussion that will broaden the learning experience for all.

Problem solving is at the core of any mathematics curriculum; it is integral to all mathematical activity. As such, it should permeate the entire mathematics program. Students who are consistently presented with challenging problems learn to develop and apply new strategies. When they are also given opportunities to communicate their strategies with others and reflect on their thinking, their problem solving abilities are further enhanced.

Middle School Reasoning and Proof

REASONING IS FUNDAMENTAL TO THE STUDY of mathematics— it is a state of mind that causes students to explore, to justify, and to validate. It permeates all content areas and all grade levels. Students are reasoning when they interpret data, when they solve problems, and when they view geometric patterns and shapes. As they are presented with new problems, they use reasoning skills to apply previously acquired information and to test the validity of their solutions. Reasoning is the process by which students make sense of mathematics.

As they develop mathematically, students learn that mathematics is a discipline based on an inherent set of rules. Reasoning begins with intuition. This intuition is used by even the youngest children in their efforts to make sense of mathematics, and it should be encouraged as the basis of reasoning at all grade levels. This informal intuition will become the basis for reasoning through representations that are more formal and for proofs based upon the rules.

What are some ways reasoning and proof can be incorporated into the mathematics class? An excellent way is to ask questions that hold students accountable for their thinking. *How did you get your answer? Tell me how you thought about that. Why does your solution work? Do you think that strategy will always work?*

Piaget believed that for students to develop reasoning, it was imperative to have social interaction. A powerful means of achieving this interaction is through mathematical discussions. Designating time during the class for students to put forth their ideas for examination is critical. Students must learn to explain and defend their thinking. They must also learn to detect unsound reasoning in explanations presented by other students. In any given class there will be a wide range of reasoning abilities and it is helpful for students with less mature reasoning to hear from those with well-developed skills. These mathematical discussions increase a student's repertoire of reasoning skills.

What do these mathematical discussions look like? A teacher typically presents a problem to the class that may be related to concepts being studied. A class of sixth grade students working on figuring percentages was presented with the following problem:

What is 75% of 80?

After allowing a few minutes for students to work independently to figure out the solution, the teacher, Mr. Matthews, invited the students to share their solutions and strategies with another classmate.

"How many of you got the same answer as the person you shared with?" Most hands were raised.

"How many of you used the exact same strategy as that person?" Fewer than half the students responded.

"O.K. Let's look at some of the ways you found to solve this problem."

Min Lee volunteered first. "I got 60. I know that 50% of 80 is 40. 25% is half of 50%. Since 50% was 40, then 25% must be half of that or 20. Then I added 40 and 20. I got 60."

"How many of you used Min Lee's method?" Several students raised their hands.

"Who can tell us another way to look at the problem?"

Jack responded. "I know that 10% of 80 is 8. In order to get 70%, I multiplied 8 × 7 and got 56. But I still need 5% more. I thought 5% is half of 10%, so 5% must be 4. By adding 56 and 4, I got 60, the same as Min Lee."

Several students indicated they were unclear, so Jack repeated the strategy elaborating on his procedure and stopping after each step to clarify.

Stephanie volunteered another method. "75% is the same as $\frac{3}{4}$. I divided 80 into fourths. Each fourth is 20. Three of them are 60."

"I changed 75% to 0.75 and multiplied. 0.75 × 80 is 60." offered Jose.

As students present their strategies, there should be opportunities to compare the methods to see how they are alike and how they are different. Students should be asked to consider which strategies they think worked best with the particular problem and why.

Discussions like the one above are rich in reasoning and proof. Whether a student is explaining his answer to the class or listening to the explanation of another to see if it makes sense, reasoning skills are being employed. The time spent on conversations like these, with thoughtful questions posed by the teacher to guide the discussion, is invaluable.

Middle School Communication

Whether between teacher and student, between a pair of students, or among groups of students, the communication skills of reading, writing, and listening and speaking provide the means for sharing ideas and promoting mathematical understanding. As students express their ideas through oral and written language, they have an opportunity to clarify their thinking and reinforce their comprehension of the concepts they are working with. By listening to explanations given by their classmates, students are exposed to ideas they may not have thought of. This provides a greater network of connections among ideas and, in turn, enhances learning.

Ample opportunities to discuss mathematical ideas should be provided. One extremely effective technique that was described in the previous section on Reasoning and Proof involves presenting an interesting problem to the class, allowing time to solve the problem, and then asking students to explain how they solved the problem. Providing a forum for a number of different solutions to be presented and defended by students results in rich dialogue. There is a very high level of mental activity associated with social interaction of this nature. Students who are afforded opportunities to take part in these mathematical conversations on a regular basis learn more effectively how to reason and defend their answers. In the process, they also learn to communicate and to clarify and refine their ideas, which leads to deeper understanding.

Elementary teachers lay the groundwork for students to develop facility in communicating their thinking. Children in the primary grades are usually interested in conversing about mathematics with the teacher as well as with others. If children in grades K–2 have had sufficient opportunities to discuss mathematical ideas, they generally are pretty comfortable continuing that pattern in grades 3–5. But all that changes in the middle school years. This period is characterized socially by wanting to fit in. Students become hesitant to put their thinking in front of others for fear of being ridiculed. Because adolescents are highly social, it becomes essential to have them work in groups. This provides them with a structured forum for their social behavior and a sense of camaraderie.

In middle school, mathematics begins to become more abstract. New concepts still need to be introduced conceptually, but students need to move from concrete representations to symbolic notation more quickly. Effective communication of ideas becomes even more important.

This portion of a 7th grade lesson offers an example of how communication was effectively used to develop an understanding of how surface area can vary for a fixed volume. Each student received 8 unit cubes and the class was led through an oral review of surface area and volume through a series of questions.

> **What is the volume of each cube?**
> **What is the total volume of the cubes?**
> **What is the surface area of each cube?**
> **What is the total surface area of the cubes?**

Students were then directed to arrange the 8 cubes in a 2 × 4 shape. Questions directed their attention to the concept being developed.

> **What is the volume of the figure you made with your cubes? Explain.**
> **Is the total surface area still 48 square units? Explain.**

As students responded to the questions, there was an opportunity to assess their ability to apply the definitions and figure volume and surface area. Any misunderstandings could be immediately addressed and corrected. Information could be expanded upon.

The lesson went on to have students work in pairs to explore other configurations using the 8 cubes and to find their surface areas and volumes and record their findings. A class discussion was held to compare the results. This led to a discussion about what configuration produced the greatest surface area and the least surface area for the same volume. Students went on to explore how symbolic representation could be used to express those relationships.

This approach allowed students to investigate a problem on a conceptual level with concrete objects and communicate understanding of the concepts involved before moving to symbolic representation. They had an opportunity to work together and communicate their ideas with each other as they investigated solutions. Their findings were then discussed in a larger group and there were opportunities to clarify, affirm, and reinforce understanding.

Putting ideas on paper is another means of helping students organize their thinking. The act of writing something down causes a student to reflect on ideas and refine them before committing that thinking to paper. Often, at the end of a lesson students will be asked to communicate what they learned in the problem or investigation they have just completed. This written reflection can be an important tool for teachers in assessing their students' mathematical understanding. Words, pictures, numbers, and symbols are all important parts of written communication that students have at their disposal, and middle school students are becoming much more adept at using mathematical symbols to communicate their thinking. Many teachers use journal writing as a way for students to relate what they know about mathematics.

Students in grades 6–8 should be provided with regular opportunities to use both oral and written language and to share mathematical ideas with their teachers and peers on a daily basis. This exchange will challenge students to reexamine or refine their thinking and will affirm understanding. This process is essential to internalizing mathematics.

Middle School Connections

MAKING CONNECTIONS IN MATHEMATICS is a three-fold process. First, connections are made when one mathematical idea is used to build another. Second, connections are made among different mathematical ideas. Third, connections are made between mathematics and contexts outside the field of mathematics.

Because mathematics is an integrated discipline, treating it as a whole body of knowledge and focusing on the connections that occur naturally adds dimension to ideas and concepts. How is counting related to addition, addition to subtraction, addition to multiplication, multiplication to area? A cohesive curriculum that is clearly articulated from pre-kindergarten through the twelfth grade, one that connects the mathematical ideas within each grade as well as the mathematics between grade levels, is critical if those connections are to take place.

Making connections to prior mathematical experiences is vital for the understanding of how mathematical ideas build on one another. Teachers need to know what mathematics students learned previously in order to build on that knowledge. In a given unit of study, attention should be paid to ensure that mathematics concepts build upon one another from day to day in a coherent manner. Teachers should also be aware of what their students will be studying in subsequent grades so they can lay the foundations for obvious connections to further studies.

Mathematics permeates other curriculum areas and it is found in the everyday experience outside of school as well. The use of shapes and patterns is prevalent in art and architecture; measurement skills and classification skills are important in science; measurement skills and knowledge of fractions are utilized in cooking and in building models; and measurement skills, data gathering, and statistics are applied in the social sciences.

In middle school, students build on the mathematical foundation laid in elementary school. The concepts of fractions, decimals, and percents were introduced informally in grades K–5, but in grades 6–8, the relationships among these forms take on greater focus. Students become aware of the similarities and differences in these representations and learn which is appropriate for a particular situation. Proportional reasoning and algebraic thinking are also major areas of study. The number work developed in intermediate grades is extended to include work with integers.

Computing with integers is a new topic for middle school students, one that can be connected to the study of number relationships that students encountered in elementary school. The number line, something all students have had experience with, is a helpful tool for modeling addition and subtraction with integers.

There are countless ways to make connections with the mathematics studied in the middle grades. For example, students enjoy taking surveys of their peers' preferences in food, music, movies, and games. This can be connected to collecting, organizing, and displaying this data in a way that makes sense, important skills that help students to better understand and interpret information presented in the world around them. Analyzing the data gathered from these surveys can be connected to interesting statistical problems. The teacher might pose the questions or have students generate their own.

Calculating the cost of having a class party that includes refreshments, prizes for games, and paper products is another relevant problem for students in grades 6–8. Such an activity makes connections to the real world and to students' estimation skills, their understanding of ratios, and their knowledge of operations with fractions and decimals. Working in teams, students can generate a menu and figure out how to adhere to a given budget. This kind of problem also encourages cost comparisons among various brands.

It is important for teachers to be conscious of connections that can be made in mathematics and to weave those connections into daily practice. When students are able to connect mathematical ideas both inside and outside of the classroom, they begin to see mathematics as a cohesive body of knowledge.

Middle School Representation

REPRESENTATIONS PROVIDE VEHICLES FOR EXPRESSING and internalizing mathematical thought. They include physical objects, pictures, and symbols; and they encompass mental images, words, and ideas as well. Representation is a critical component in shaping the way students access, understand, express, and utilize mathematical ideas

Representations can be formal or informal. Examples of formal representations are the conventional symbols, graphs, diagrams, and so on traditionally introduced in school mathematics. More informal forms are often invented by students as a way of making sense of mathematical ideas and communicating those ideas to classmates or the teacher. Connecting to these informal forms will facilitate a meaningful transition to thinking and communicating in the language of mathematics.

As teachers design lessons, choosing the type of representations they feel will best help students understand a concept becomes an important consideration. What shared mathematical language is needed to effectively communicate ideas? What manipulatives or models will be appropriate? How will students record their understanding of the concept? When is it appropriate to move from physical to symbolic representations?

Students at the middle-school level use informal methods to help them interpret ideas that are more complex. For example, before introducing the formula for finding the volume of rectangular solids, a teacher might assign the following task to groups of four:

> Using centimeter cubes, build a variety of rectangular solids. Record the length, width, and height of each one you build. Also, record the number of cubes used to build each figure.

As the students build their solids and record information, the teacher can move among the groups asking questions. The lesson can conclude with a discussion about the relationships between the dimensions of the solids and the number of cubes used to build them. Students share the charts they made which clearly show that the number of centimeters used was equal to the length times the width times the height of the solid.

Rectangular Solids

Length	Width	Height	Total Cubes
2	2	2	8
3	2	2	12
3	3	2	18
3	3	3	27
4	3	2	24
4	4	2	32
4	4	3	48
4	4	4	64

The students are then ready to be presented with the symbolic representation $V = l \times w \times h$, the formula used to find the volume of a rectangular solid.

In this example, using physical representation by building models provides direct experience with the relationships among the length, width, and height and the volume of a figure. This allows students to establish a mental representation of the relationships, so the abstract equation will make sense to them. These students are much more likely to remember the formula.

Conclusion

The process standards are not an end in, and of, themselves. Rather, they provide the advanced organizers, or plan, for lessons that present important mathematics content. Seeing connections among mathematical topics enables students to reason and make sense of new ideas and problem-solving situations they encounter. Through the process of communication, students are able to represent these new ideas either formally or informally.

Just as process standards are interrelated, so are the process and content standards. For true mathematical thinking and learning to occur, both process and content need to be skillfully woven into and through each lesson. That is the goal to work toward.

Standard 1 Number and Operation

AT THE SEVENTH GRADE LEVEL, number and operation includes work with fractions and the four basic operations, ratio and proportion problems, percents, and integers. Our lessons are derived from these important topics, and include a lesson that focuses on multiplying fractions, a lesson on recognizing proportion problems, a lesson that explores percents, and a lesson that develops integer concepts.

Three lessons model how the process standards can be used to teach content. A fourth lesson is a hypothetical textbook lesson that we have revised to be more standards based. These four lessons do not represent the entire curriculum, but rather provide glimpses of how, with a more concentrated effort to incorporate the process standards, better mathematics teaching and learning can be achieved.

One lesson we have chosen develops a better understanding of the algorithm for multiplying fractions. Instead of being taught strictly as a rote procedure, students draw several representations of "fraction-of-fraction" situations. By shading the correct parts of the whole, students can obtain the product visually. Students use reasoning and proof to generalize how the same results can be obtained from the several examples and make the connections to the algorithm.

Another lesson we have chosen is a lesson that focuses on recognizing whether or not a problem can be solved using a proportion. Students have solved proportions, but were not asked to consider whether a problem might not be solved using a proportion. This lesson relies on the process standard of communication to focus students on identifying the clues that might indicate whether or not a proportion should be used, and then discuss these in groups and as a class.

A third lesson we have chosen is a lesson that explores the three different types of percent problems. Students make connections to their own experiences with percent and to their prior knowledge of fractions, decimals, and ratios. This lesson is problem-solving based, as students are asked to come up with their own methods to solve the different types of percent problems. Students use reasoning and proof to generalize that percent is calculated from the whole, and to support their methods for solving.

The hypothetical textbook lesson we have chosen to revise is one that introduces the concept of integers and how to compare integers. Many standard lessons approach this topic using the definition of "opposite" and showing a horizontal number line. In this revised lesson, more connections are made to students' experiences with integers, and opportunities are provided for students to discuss these. More representations are shown, such as a vertical number line for temperature.

Standard 1 Lessons

Multiplying Fractions

Recognizing Proportion Problems

Exploring Percents

Understanding Integers

Multiplying Fractions

Introduction

Objective → Students will understand and explain why the standard algorithm for multiplying fractions works.

Context → Students build on their basic understanding of fractions and whole number multiplication to multiply fractions. They will go on to multiplying mixed numbers.

NCTM Standards Focus

Students are often taught to multiply fractions as a simple procedure of multiplying the numerators and the denominators. Sometimes an illustration is presented, though not always with an explanation. A standards-based lesson would have students focus at least as much on understanding why the algorithm works, in addition to the mechanics of doing it. By incorporating the following three process standards into a lesson, students will understand more about the algorithm for multiplying fractions.

Representation Students make several drawings of "fraction-of-fraction" situations. Students then represent these situations as multiplication problems.

Reasoning and Proof Students come to realize from their drawings why the denominators are multiplied and why the numerators are multiplied when multiplying fractions.

Connections Students make connections between the visual models and the symbolic representation of multiplying fractions. They also connect the use of the word "of" to indicate multiplication.

Teaching Plan

Materials → Student pages 22–23; two colored pencils

BEGIN THE LESSON BY PRESENTING the problem "How much is $\frac{4}{5}$ of $\frac{2}{3}$?" Allow students to work in pairs. Offer the suggestion that they may want to use their colored pencils to make a drawing of the problem. This will provide students with a visual representation of the situation, which is likely the only way in which they would be able to come up with an answer.

Observe students as they work. If any pairs are unsure of how to begin, suggest that since the problem asks them to find $\frac{4}{5}$ of $\frac{2}{3}$, that they should first draw $\frac{2}{3}$. Have students draw a rectangle. *How many equal sized pieces should there be?* (3) *How many should you shade in with the colored pencil?* (2)

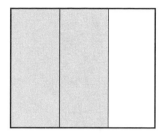

The next step for students is to find $\frac{4}{5}$ of the $\frac{2}{3}$. If students are having difficulty at this point, suggest that they think of the $\frac{2}{3}$ as the whole. This can be visualized by covering up the $\frac{1}{3}$ that is not shaded (and covering the line between the shaded $\frac{2}{3}$, if necessary). *To show $\frac{4}{5}$, how many equal sized pieces should this new whole be divided into?* (5) *How many pieces should be shaded?* (4) Suggest that the new lines be drawn perpendicular to the ones drawn to show the $\frac{2}{3}$.

What Might Happen . . . What to Do

At this point, some students might come up with an answer of $\frac{8}{11}$. Remind them that in order for the denominator to be 11, there must be 11 equal sized pieces. Ask them if their drawing shows 11 equal sized pieces. (It doesn't.)

In order to determine an answer, the denominator of the fraction must represent a number of equal sized pieces. The current drawing does not show all equal sized pieces. *How can this be accomplished?* (Extend the lines for the fifths into the unshaded third.) *How many equal sized pieces are there in the rectangle now?* (15) *How many pieces were shaded twice?* (8) *How much is $\frac{4}{5}$ of $\frac{2}{3}$?* $\left(\frac{8}{15}\right)$

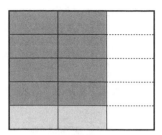

Have students do two more of these problems, such as finding $\frac{5}{6}$ of $\frac{1}{2}$ and $\frac{3}{8}$ of $\frac{3}{5}$. Provide the same types of prompts as from the first problem to students who might still need them.

After the problems have been completed, show the solutions to the class. Show how their visual models should look, and write the results next to the diagrams: $\frac{4}{5}$ of $\frac{2}{3}$ is $\frac{8}{15}$, $\frac{5}{6}$ of $\frac{1}{2}$ is $\frac{5}{12}$, and $\frac{3}{8}$ of $\frac{2}{5}$ is $\frac{6}{40}$, which should be reduced to $\frac{3}{20}$. Emphasize that answers should be reduced whenever possible. The method of canceling will likely be presented in a future lesson.

Ask students to examine the results. Students should notice that the numerators and the denominators of the results are the products of the numerators and denominators of the two fractions.

This is where reasoning and proof plays its role in helping students to make the important connections in this lesson. Ask students why it makes sense for the numerators and denominators to be multiplied to give correct answers.

Multiplying the denominators makes sense because when fifths and thirds are intersected, fifteenths should be the result; when sixths and halves are intersected, twelfths should be the result; and when eighths and fifths are intersected, fortieths should be the result.

Multiplying the numerators makes sense because where the shadings overlap is a rectangular region that has the two numerators for dimensions. In the first problem, the shadings overlap in a 2 × 4 rectangle, in the second problem the shadings overlap in a 5 × 1 rectangle, and in the third problem the shadings overlap in a 3 × 2 rectangle.

There are two more connections to be made. One is that the word "of" is an indicator for multiplication. Students may be familiar with this from percent applications.

The other connection relates to number sense. Students generally associate multiplication with quantities that get larger, but when both numbers are proper fractions, the answer is less than either factor. Students sometimes have difficulty grasping that $\frac{1}{2} \times \frac{1}{2}$ is $\frac{1}{4}$. Making a drawing of $\frac{1}{2}$ of $\frac{1}{2}$ can help to make this point clearer.

Students should now have a better understanding of why, when multiplying fractions, it is correct to multiply the numerators and the denominators to get the answer.

Student Pages

Student page 22 has students make drawings to find the answers to problems similar to those presented during the lesson. Student page 23 asks students to multiply some fractions, and to think of some situations in which problems like these might be applied.

Assessment

Assessment during the lesson came while observing students working on the problems presented and then by evaluating their participation in the following class discussion. The student pages may also be used to gauge individual progress.

NCTM Standards Summary

Students used representation as they drew models showing a fraction of a fraction. They used reasoning and proof to analyze several results and determine how the results were obtained. They made connections to the algorithm for multiplying fractions. Students also made connections between the word "of" and the operation of multiplication, and to the number sense idea that multiplying two fractions results in an answer that is less than either fraction.

Answers

Page 22
Possible drawings shown.

1. $\frac{3}{20}$

2. $\frac{1}{10}$

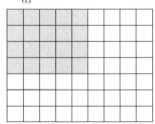

3. $\frac{20}{63}$

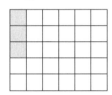

4. $\frac{4}{9}$

Page 23

1. $\frac{4}{15}$

2. $\frac{1}{6}$

3. $\frac{1}{4}$

4. $\frac{1}{14}$

5. $\frac{16}{27}$

6. $\frac{7}{44}$

7 and 8. Answers will vary.

Multiplying Fractions

Make a drawing to solve each problem.

❶ $\frac{3}{4}$ of $\frac{1}{5}$

❷ $\frac{1}{6}$ of $\frac{3}{5}$

❸ $\frac{5}{9}$ of $\frac{4}{7}$

❹ $\frac{2}{3}$ of $\frac{2}{3}$

Standard 1 Number and Operation

Multiplying Fractions

Solve the problem.
Reduce answers whenever possible.

1 $\frac{1}{3} \times \frac{4}{5} =$ _____

2 $\frac{3}{4} \times \frac{2}{9} =$ _____

3 $\frac{5}{6} \times \frac{3}{10} =$ _____

4 $\frac{1}{2} \times \frac{1}{7} =$ _____

5 $\frac{2}{3} \times \frac{8}{9} =$ _____

6 $\frac{1}{4} \times \frac{7}{11} =$ _____

7 Create a situation in which you would have to find a fraction of a fraction. Give the answer to your question.

8 Create another situation in which you would have to find a fraction of a fraction. Give the answer to your question.

Recognizing Proportion Problems

Introduction

Objective → Students will recognize and solve problems that can be solved using a proportion.

Context → Students have learned about ratios and generating equivalent ratios. They may have solved proportion problems using cross products. After this lesson, students will move on to solving proportion problems.

NCTM Standards Focus

In many presentations of proportions, students are given a definition, asked to identify proportions using cross products, and then asked to set up and solve problems using proportions. What is generally omitted is how to identify whether or not a problem can be solved using a proportion. Focusing on the following three process standards, this lesson provides students with opportunities to analyze and recognize problems that can be solved using a proportion.

Connections Students draw on their prior knowledge of fractions and ratio as it relates to proportion problems.

Representation Representation is important as students find that writing ratios as fractions is the most useful way to set up and solve proportion problems.

Communication Students have to read problems carefully and try to identify the clues that indicate whether a problem could be solved using a proportion. Students share these clues with each other and make them a part of their own knowledge.

Teaching Plan

Materials → Student pages 28–29

BEGIN THE LESSON BY HAVING STUDENTS discuss what they know about proportions. Anything having to do with proportion is valuable—a definition, contextual examples, or a way to solve a particular problem. Students here are making connections to their prior experiences.

Bring students together for a class discussion of their ideas about proportion. Some examples of what students may say are:

- I spend a large proportion of my time doing homework.(informal) I would like to keep the time I spend doing homework in proportion to the time I spend on my hobbies.
- The amount of water to flour in the recipe should be in proportion to the amount of vinegar to oil.
- The number of 7th graders to 8th graders on the student council should be in proportion to the number of 7th to 8th graders in the entire school.

As students present examples of proportion, point out the difference between examples based on informal conversation and those that are acceptable in terms of the mathematical definition. Ask students to analyze all their examples of proportion and to restate them in terms of the mathematical definition, as two equal ratios.

CONTINUE THE LESSON by presenting this problem to the class.

> An architect is drawing a plan for an outdoor garden on centimeter-grid paper. He allows 2 centimeters on the grid to represent 3 meters in the garden. He draws a line 19 centimeters long on the grid paper to represent one side of the garden. How long is that side in the actual garden?

Ask students not to solve the problem, but to determine whether or not the problem could be solved using a proportion, and to explain why or why not. It is this explanation of *why?* or *why not?* that really brings in what the standards are trying to achieve.

Have students share their thoughts. The point that you would like to emerge is that the problem involves *equivalent ratios*, or *equivalent comparisons*. In the problem, 2 cm to 3 m is one ratio $(\frac{2}{3})$, and 19 cm to an unknown number of meters is its equivalent ratio $(\frac{19}{n})$. Representation is important here as the ratios in the problem are not presented in fractional form, but need to be written as fractions in order to form the proportion.

Now asks students how they might solve the problem since they now know that $\frac{2}{3} = \frac{19}{n}$. Have them work with a partner and then present their solution methods to the entire class.

Methods Students Might Use

Method 1 Since $\frac{2}{3} = \frac{19}{n}$, $\frac{3}{2} = \frac{n}{19}$. Multiply both sides of the equation by 19 to get $19 \times \frac{3}{2} = n$. $28.5 = n$.

Method 2 Divide 19 by 2 and get 9.5, multiply that by 3 to get 28.5.

Now present this problem to the class.

> A bag contains a mixture of red and blue cubes. There are 5 red cubes for every 7 blue cubes. If the bag contains 91 blue cubes, how many red cubes are there in the bag?

f.y.i.

It is important to note that the mathematical definition of *proportion* varies somewhat from the way the word is used informally. A dictionary defines *proportion* as *"a part considered in relation to its whole."* However, the mathematical definition is *two equal ratios.*

Again, ask students not to solve the problem, but to determine whether or not it can be solved using a proportion. Ask them to explain why or why not.

Ideally, students will realize that there are equivalent ratios, or comparisons, here. There are 5 red cubes for every 7 blue cubes ($\frac{5}{7}$) and an unknown number of red cubes to 91 blue cubes ($\frac{n}{91}$).

Have students work with a partner to solve the problem and then discuss solutions as a class. (The answer is 65 red cubes.)

THE FOLLOWING PROBLEM WILL HELP you make sure that students are not just making a ratio and then going on to make a proportion where one does not exist.

> A rectangle has a length of 10 cm. The perimeter of the rectangle is 28 cm and the area is 40 cm². What is the width of the rectangle?

Students should realize that whatever ratio they choose to write, there is not a second ratio that is equivalent. This problem cannot be solved using a proportion. (Width = 4 cm)

The following percent problem brings up an interesting point.

> There were 50 questions on a test. Three students answered 40 of the questions correctly. What percent of the problems did the students get correct?

It may seem like there is not a proportion here but there is one that is implied: $\frac{40}{50} = \frac{n}{100}$. Make sure students understand that 100 is always the whole in a percent ratio.

To conclude the lesson, have students work in pairs to solve the following problems. Ask students to first determine whether or not they can use a proportion to solve the problems, then have them solve them.

> *Problem 1.* A laundry has a service called "wash and fold" in which laundry is weighed, washed, and folded. Charges are calculated by the pound. Last week Rich had 11 pounds of laundry washed and folded for $16.39. If he takes 9 pounds to the same laundry this week, what should he expect to pay?

This problem can be solved using a proportion. ($\frac{11}{16.39} = \frac{9}{x}$; $x = \$1.49$ per pound.)

Problem 2. In basketball, a regular field goal is worth 2 points. The Blazers took 35 regular field goal shots and made 25 of them. How many points did they score with regular field goals?

This problem cannot be solved using a proportion. $(25 \times 2 = 50)$

Student Pages

Student page 28 asks students to decide whether or not the problems can be solved using proportions. Student page 29 asks students to write problems that can be solved using proportions and to explain how they know when a problem can be solved using a proportion.

Assessment

You have observed students in class discussions and as they worked in pairs or small groups applying their knowledge of ratio to explore the concept of proportions. You had opportunities to evaluate their understanding as they explained whether or not problems could be solved using proportions. You also had opportunities to assess understanding as students presented their solution methods.

NCTM Standards Summary

Students used communication in group and class discussions, focusing on how to recognize problems that can be solved with proportions. They made connections as they drew on their prior experience to build their understanding of proportions. They made new connections as they wrote equivalent ratios in order to solve proportion problems. Students used representation as they interpreted ratios, wrote the ratios as fractions, and wrote the proportions that they used to solve the problems.

Answers

Page 28

1. $\frac{20}{50} = \frac{12}{x}$, 30 inches

2. Not a proportion

3. $\frac{3}{4} = \frac{8}{x}$, $10\frac{2}{3}$ cups of milk

4. $\frac{1}{50} = \frac{8}{x}$, 400 miles

5. Not a proportion

6. Not a proportion

7. $\frac{5}{7} = \frac{x}{1}$, $\frac{5}{7}$ of a gallon

8. $\frac{3}{5} = \frac{x}{345}$, 207 girls

Page 29

1–7. Answers will vary.

Recognizing Proportion Problems

Read each problem. Decide whether or not you can use a proportion to solve it.
Solve the problems for which there is a proportion.

❶ A game board is 20 inches wide by 50 inches long. You want to make a smaller version of the board with a width of 12 inches. How long should the board be?

❷ You have a square with an 8-inch side. You want to draw a triangle with a base 3 times greater than a side of the square. What is the altitude of the triangle?

❸ The recipe calls for milk and flour in a 3 to 4 ratio. How many cups of flour do you need if you use 8 cups of milk?

❹ A map shows that 1 inch represents 50 miles. How many miles does 8 inches represent?

❺ If it snows 3 inches in 1 hour, how much snow does the department of public services have to remove?

❻ The warmest day last summer was 106°F and the coldest was 59°F. What was the average high temperature last summer?

❼ The painter mixed the green paint using a 2 to 5 ratio of blue to yellow paint. How much yellow paint is there in 1 gallon of green paint?

❽ There are 345 students in the school. There are 2 boys for every 3 girls. How many girls are in the school?

Standard 1 Number and Operation

Recognizing Proportion Problems

Write six problems that can be solved using proportions.
Write the proportion that can be used to solve the problem.

❶

❷

❸

❹

❺

❻

❼ Explain how you can tell when a problem can be solved using a proportion.

Exploring Percents

Introduction

Objective → Students will explore percent problems using previous knowledge of fractions and decimals. They will develop a conceptual understanding that different percent situations require different solution methods.

Context → Students have a working knowledge of fractions and decimals as ratios and real numbers, and how to perform the operations with these numbers. They read, write, and understand the basic concept of percent. Students will apply the informal knowledge of percent gained in this lesson to the formal algorithms they will encounter in future lessons.

NCTM Standards Focus

Often when students encounter percent, they are presented with rules and algorithms to memorize. Rather than concentrate on the problem, students focus on which rule to apply. In this standards-based lesson, students explore conceptually how to solve different types of percent problems. By incorporating the process standards, students will understand more about solving percent problems than just knowing an algorithm.

Problem Solving Students relate their previous mathematical knowledge of fractions, decimals, and percent to problem situations in percent. They represent different situations in percent and determine different ways to approach the problems.

Reasoning and Proof Students generalize from the three given percent situations that percent is always calculated on the whole. Students also support their methods for solving the problems.

Connections Students make connections to their prior knowledge of fractions, decimals, and ratios. Connections are also made relating percents to real-world experiences and situations.

Teaching Plan

Materials → Student pages 34–35

ASK STUDENTS TO GIVE EXAMPLES of when they have encountered percents. Some possible examples are listed.

- The sales tax rate is 8%.
- A store advertises "40% off."
- A savings account earns 3% interest.
- A glass of orange juice will give you 100% of the recommended daily allowance of vitamin C.
- I scored 90% on a test.

After listing a few, discuss what the percents refer to—what is the whole, and what is the part. For the test score, the whole is the total number of points possible and the part is the number of points earned. For the sales tax rate, the whole is the subtotal (the total cost of the items) and the part is the amount of the sales tax.

CONTINUE THE LESSON by telling students that you are going to give them some percent problems to work. Discuss that in percent problems, problems are different based on what information you know and don't know. For example, in the case of the 8% sales tax, if you knew that the subtotal was $50, you could figure out how much tax would be charged (the part is unknown). Or, if you knew that the amount of the sales tax was $1.50, you could determine the subtotal of the purchases (the whole is unknown).

Tell students that they have two goals in working with the three problems that you will give them. The first is to categorize the problem. They should tell what they know and what they need to find out. Have them label the problem as "percent," "part," or "whole," depending on which is the unknown. The second goal is to figure out a method to solve each problem.

Have students work together in pairs or small groups. Give them student page 34, which contains the three problems. Observe students as they work. Make sure they categorize and write what they know and what they don't know and then solve the problem. If students are having difficulty, try to have them identify whether the known information and the unknown information is the part, the whole, or the percent.

Do not provide rules and procedures for solving the problems. Encourage students to make sense of the problem first and then use number sense and what they know about percents, fractions, and decimals to solve the problems. Reassure them that informal methods that they can explain are fine. It is important that they record the discussions in their groups as well as the steps they take to solve the problems.

When students have finished, discuss both what they understood about the problems and how they solved them. What follows are some explanations and solutions.

Problem 1

In this problem we know the percentage, the test score, and we know the part, the number of problems correct. What we do not know is the whole, or the number that is 100%. Students should see that 80% is equal to the 32 problems but they do not know the number of problems that makes 100%.

Solution Methods

A. One method is to think of parts. Since the student got 80 of 100 he or
    she also got 8 of 10 or 4 of 5. That means we could look at 80% and say
    it has 4 parts–20%, 20%, 20%, and 20%. We can do the same with 32
    and see that it has 4 parts–each of them being 8. Since we need only one
    more part to make the total, that is 32 plus 8 which equals 40.

B. Another method is using fractions and multiplication. $\frac{80}{100}$ of the total is
    32. $\frac{80}{100}$ times what is 32? $80x = 3200$. x is 40.

Problem 2

In this problem we know the percentage that the student got correct and
the total number of problems. What we don't know is what number or part
of the total is correct.

Solution Methods

A. One method is to use fractions. We know that 75% is $\frac{3}{4}$. $\frac{3}{4}$ of 40 is 30.

B. Other methods might be variations of the first one. You can take half of
    40 and get 20, that is 50%. Then half of 20 is 10, that is 25%. Adding the
    two together you get 30, which is 75%.

Problem 3

In this problem we know what number makes up the part and what number
makes up the whole. However, we need to find out what percentage the part
is of the whole.

Solution Methods

A. We know the total is 40 and we need to find what percentage 36 is of the
    whole. $\frac{36}{40} = \frac{n}{100}$ or $36 = n\%$ of 40

    If you have time, ask students how they could use this solution method if
    the person got 38 problems correct. They could take 2 which is 5% (half
    of ten percent when they reached 36).

B. Find the decimal equivalent of $\frac{36}{40}$, which is 0.9, and multiply it by 100.

To end the lesson, have students generalize about the different types of percent problems.

- Sometimes you know the percent and either the part it represents or the number that represents the whole, and are asked to find the whole or the part.

- Other times you know the part and the whole and need to determine the percent.

- One ratio is the part to the whole, and the percent is an equivalent ratio with 100 as the whole.

Student Pages

Student page 34 has the three percent problems to be used for the in-class activity. Student page 35 may be assigned for homework. Encourage students to show their work with drawings and written commentary. If time allows, have them form groups to share their strategies with each other.

Assessment

As students worked to solve the problems and explain their methods, you could determine whether they understood how to set up percent problems. You were also able to observe whether they applied their prior knowledge of fractions, decimals, and percent. You can use student page 35 as a further measure of individual student's progress.

NCTM Standards Summary

Students used problem-solving strategies and connected their previous knowledge of fractions, decimals, and percent with new mathematical problem situations. They used reasoning to generalize and classify the three different percent situations. They also used reasoning to support their solution methods.

Answers

Page 34
1. 40 problems.
2. 30 problems.
3. 90%

Page 35
1. $15 = 100\%$, $\frac{3}{15}$ = mark-down
   $3 \div 15 = 0.2$ or 20%.
2. If the price is reduced by 30%, then $10.50 = 70\%$. $\frac{70}{100}$ of the original price = $10.50. $10.50 \div .70 = \$15$. The original price was $15.
3. 75% of $15 = $\frac{75}{100}$ of 15 = $.75 \times 15 = \$11.25$.
4. $75 - 45 = 30$ students in computer lab. $\frac{30}{75} = \frac{2}{5} = .40$, or 40%. 40% of the students have computer lab.
5. If 40% go to computer lab, then 60% have art.
6. $\frac{60}{75}$ of the students take the bus. $60 \div 75 = 0.80$ or 80%. $100\% - 80\% = 20\%$.

Exploring Percents

Solve each problem. Record your methods.

1 You are taking a math test and you get 32 problems, or 80%, correct on the test. How many problems are on the test?

2 Your best friend takes a math test with 40 problems. Your friend solves 75% of the problems correctly. How many problems did your friend get correct?

3 Another friend gets 36 out of 40 problems correct. What percent did your friend solve correctly?

Standard 1 Number and Operation

Exploring Percents

Solve each problem. Show your work.
Include drawings if you like.

1 Tony bought a CD on sale for $3 off the original price of $15. What percent was the CD marked down?

2 Serena got the same CD for $10.50 at another store. This was 30% off the regular price. What was the original price?

3 Erik bought a book of mystery stories. It was 25% off the original price of $15. How much did Erik pay for the book?

4 There are 75 students in the seventh grade. 45 students go to art class. The rest of the students have computer lab. What percent of the students have computer lab?

5 What percent of the students have art?

6 Sixty of the 75 seventh grade students take the bus to and from school. What percent do NOT take the bus?

Understanding Integers

Introduction

Objective → Students will understand what integers are and will compare integers.

Context → The lesson occurs at the beginning of a unit about integers. Lessons that follow cover properties and operations with integers.

Understanding Integers

Learn

Find a Pattern. Work in groups. Give a word that means the opposite. For example, for the word "in," you could write "out."

above	big	cold	north	low
soft	dark	lose	slow	up

Talk

The distance between a number and zero is its absolute value. The opposite of ⁺5 is ⁻5. They are both the same distance from zero. The absolute value of a number is its distance from zero. The absolute value of ⁺5 is 5; the absolute value of ⁻5 is 5.

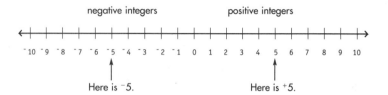

You can compare two integers on a number line. A number that is to the right of another number is the greater number. You can see that ⁻2 is greater than ⁻4 because it is farther to the right.

Try

Write the opposite of each number.

1. ⁺4   2. ⁻2   3. ⁻7
4. ⁻9   5. ⁺3   6. ⁻8

NCTM Process Standards Analysis and Focus

The standards analysis examines how the process standards have been incorporated into the above lesson. By increasing the focus on three of the process standards, a more effective and meaningful lesson can be presented. The suggestions offered can help you to think about how this might be accomplished.

Connections English language word opposites are used to introduce the concept of opposite integers. The lesson presented does not take advantage of students' prior experiences with negative numbers.

Suggestion → **Make connections to familiar real-world situations such as temperature, sports, and money to provide a frame of reference throughout the lesson. Realizing they already know**

•••

Practice

Name the letter where each integer should go.

1. ⁻5

2. ⁺3

3. ⁺4

4. ⁻2

5. The integer greater than ⁻3 but less than ⁻1.

6. The integer greater than 0 but less than 2.

Write <, >, or = for each _____.

7. ⁺4 _____ ⁻4

8. ⁺2 _____ ⁻5

9. ⁻3 _____ ⁻2

10. ⁻6 _____ ⁻6

11. ⁻200 _____ ⁻700

12. ⁺8 _____ ⁺8

Problem Solving

Use the number line on the previous page to help you solve each problem.

13. You are at ⁺2. You go 3 numbers to the left. Where are you?

14. You are at ⁻2. You go 3 numbers to the left and then go 2 numbers to the right. Where are you?

15. You are at ⁺5. You go 8 numbers to the left and then go 7 numbers to the right. Where are you?

16. You are at ⁺1. You go 5 numbers to the right and then go 6 numbers to left. Where are you?

Math Reasoning

17. The opposite of a negative integer is a _____.

18. The opposite of a positve integer is a _____.

19. Zero is neither _____ nor _____.

about and use integers will help dispel students' notions that working with negative numbers will be difficult.

Communication Opportunities in the lesson for students to interact or exchange ideas, either in discussing or in writing about integers, are limited.

Suggestion → Increase discussion about what integers are and how they are used. Discussing strategies for

determining the relative value of integers will help students gain a deeper understanding of this set of numbers. Having students explain their method(s) of comparing integers will help them become better problem-solvers.

Representation The only visual representation presented is a horizontal number line labeled to show positive and negative numbers and zero.

Suggestion → Provide a variety of visual representations, including horizontal number lines, vertical scales on thermometers, and sea level bar graphs to help students visualize integer relationships and compare numbers.

Problem Solving The exercise on the text pages labeled problem solving is actually a number-line exercise.

Reasoning and Proof The reasoning questions on these pages involve comprehension, but reasoning, generalization, and justification of thinking are not required.

The teaching plan that follows shows how the suggestions for increasing the focus on the process standards can be implemented.

Revised Teaching Plan

BEGIN THE LESSON WITH A QUICK REVIEW of counting (natural) numbers and whole numbers (all the counting numbers plus zero). *Are all the numbers you use positive? What other kinds of numbers are there?* (Fractions, decimals, negatives, and so on) *What is something that could be described using negative numbers?* Accept one or two examples, and then ask: *What term do we use to describe pairs of words such as positive/negative, up/down, gain/lose, and so on?* (opposites)

Form groups comprised of three or four students. Instruct students to compile lists of familiar opposite situations that might be described using positive and negative numbers. As they make these real-world connections, students will see that they already have experience with negative numbers and that these numbers are quite useful.

BRING THE CLASS TOGETHER. List students' responses on the board. Some typical situations may include temperatures above or below zero, elevation above or below sea level, changes in stock prices, deposits or withdrawals of money, or gains and losses of yardage in football. Prompt individual students to explain why they used positive and negative numbers for these situations.

Have students explain what a positive number means and what a negative number means in each situation. For example, with temperature $^-5°$ means 5° below zero (or a drop of 5 degrees) and $^+5°$ means 5° above zero (or a rise of 5 degrees). Emphasize that the positive and negative changes are in relation to a given starting point and often this starting point is zero. By formulating their own explanations and communicating their ideas, students will better understand what integers mean and how they are related, and they will gain experience in using integer terminology.

HELP STUDENTS VISUALIZE RELATIONSHIPS among integers with various representations. Football yardages can be shown on a horizontal number line, while temperatures on a thermometer provide a representation

f.y.i.

Mathematicians have used different notations for negative numbers. The Hindus used a dot or a small circle over a number to show that it was negative; for example, $\overset{\bullet}{3}$ or $\overset{\circ}{3}$ represented $^-3$. The Chinese, who are credited with the first formal uses of negative numbers, used red to show a positive number and black to show a negative number. (Compare this tradition with modern accounting usage where "in the black" indicates profits and "in the red" indicates losses.) The sixteenth-century Italian mathematician Cardano used the letter *m*, probably for "minus," to show negatives, and so $^-8$ was written m:8.

on a vertical number line. A bar graph showing elevations such as 800 feet above sea level and 300 feet below sea level is another effective visual representation.

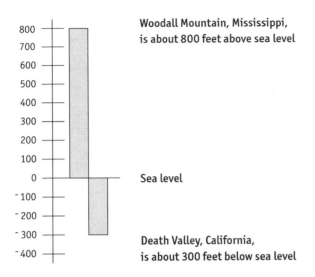

800 —
700 —
600 —
500 —
400 —
300 —
200 —
100 —

Woodall Mountain, Mississippi, is about 800 feet above sea level

0 — **Sea level**

⁻100 —
⁻200 —
⁻300 —
⁻400 —

Death Valley, California, is about 300 feet below sea level

Draw a number line on the board. Define the set of integers as the whole numbers and their opposites. Explain that opposite integers are the same distance from zero but in different directions, like east-west travel on a road. Have students describe where the negative integers are on the number line and how they are arranged. Ask them to suggest several pairs of opposite integers. Then ask students to explain why each of the following is or isn't an integer: 7 (yes), ⁻19 (yes) $3\frac{1}{2}$ (no), ⁻15.5 (no).

CONTINUE HAVING STUDENTS ANSWER QUESTIONS to help them understand how different sets of numbers are related. *Are all integers also decimal numbers?* (Yes. Decimal numbers are any numbers, positive or negative, that can be expressed with a decimal point.) *Are all decimal numbers also integers?* (No. Integers are whole numbers and their inverses.) *Are all integers also fractions?* (Yes.) *Are all fractions also integers?* (No.)

Next, make a connection to students' prior knowledge by asking them to explain how they determine which of two whole numbers on a number line is greater. (The number to the right is greater.) Ask if this same rule can be used to compare negative numbers. (Yes.) Have one student name two integers, and show these integers on a number line. Ask another student to explain the reasoning for deciding which is greater. To get students to think more deeply about order on a number line, have them explain whether or not a negative integer can ever be greater than a positive integer.

INITIATE A DISCUSSION OF ABSOLUTE VALUE by highlighting the numbers ⁺4 and ⁻4. *Locate ⁺4 and ⁻4 on the number line. What can you tell me about these two numbers?* (⁺4 is 4 units to the right of zero; ⁻4 is 4 units to the left of zero.) Point out that the positions of both numbers were described as "4 units to . . ." and *not* "negative 4 units to . . . ." Explain that the distance from zero is always stated as a positive number and the sign indicates the direction. A simple illustration such as the one shown can be presented to visually reinforce the concept. Summarize by defining *absolute value* as the distance a number is from zero on a number line. Check students' understanding by having them give the absolute value for several integers on the number line.

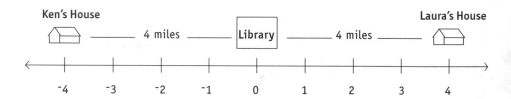

CONCLUDE THE LESSON by helping students develop a better understanding of absolute value, which is a difficult concept. Pose questions and ask that students explain their thinking as they answer. *How many numbers have an absolute value of 6? What are the numbers? What is the absolute value of zero? How many numbers have an absolute value of zero? Is the absolute value of a number ever negative?* Challenge question: *If the absolute value of a number* A *is greater than the absolute value of a number* B, *is* A *always greater than* B? *Prove your answer using a number line and give examples.*

What Might Happen . . . What to Do

Students frequently have difficulty comparing two negative integers such as ⁻8 and ⁻11 because they do not fully understand the concept of negativity. They may write ⁻11 > ⁻8 because they know 11 > 8. Using a thermometer is helpful in correcting this error. Have students locate both negative numbers. The lower integer is the "colder" or lesser temperature. Hence, ⁻11° is less than ⁻8°, so ⁻11 < ⁻8.

Student Pages

Students should now be ready to complete exercises similar to those on the reduced student pages.

Assessment

As students described real-world situations, answered questions about opposites, and explained how to compare integers, there were opportunities to assess their understanding of the set of integers and integer relationships. It was possible to evaluate how well students understood absolute value as they responded to oral exercises.

NCTM Standards Summary

By making connections to real-world situations such as football, money, and temperature, students gained a better understanding of the meaning of integers. The lesson also gave students opportunities to communicate their ideas about the relationship of opposite integers and methods of comparing integers. Representations of integers on number lines, thermometers, and bar graphs provided the students with visual reinforcement of how integers are arranged and helped them develop their skills of comparing numbers and finding absolute value.

© Creative Publications

Standard 2 **Algebra**

AT THE SEVENTH GRADE LEVEL, algebra includes a lot of work with algebraic expressions and equations, and analyzing patterns. Our lessons are derived from these important topics, and include a lesson on simplifying expressions, a lesson using equations, a lesson on using patterns to solve problems, and a lesson on translating algebraic expressions.

Three lessons model how the process standards can be used to teach content. A fourth lesson is a hypothetical textbook lesson that we have revised to be more standards based. These four lessons do not represent the entire curriculum, but rather provide glimpses of how, with a more concentrated effort to incorporate the process standards, better mathematics teaching and learning can be achieved.

One lesson we have chosen focuses on simplifying expressions. Rather than simply define and practice combining like terms, students model real-world situations algebraically to help them understand when terms can be combined and when they cannot. Reasoning and proof is emphasized here as students generalize from these situations to their own rules for simplifying expressions.

Another lesson we have chosen has students translate a problem situation into an equation with a variable, and solve it. Through the process standards of representation, communication, and connections, students begin to see the value of using an equation to represent and solve a real-world problem. Students solve the equations using tables and graphs.

A third lesson we have chosen is one in which students solve problems by identifying and continuing a pattern. Driven by the process standards of reasoning and proof, representation, and problem-solving, students solve real-world problems by analyzing and extending patterns. Students show patterns geometrically, in tables, or algebraically, and have to explain how they used patterns to obtain their solution.

The hypothetical textbook lesson that we have chosen to revise is a lesson on translating algebraic expressions. Through better incorporation of the process standards of connections, reasoning and proof, and communication, students develop a more complete list of phrases and the operations the phrases indicate. Students also learn that they can substitute values into their algebraic expressions to see if the result makes sense with the written expression.

Standard 2 Lessons

Simplifying Expressions

Using Equations

Analyzing Patterns

Translating Algebraic Expressions

Simplifying Expressions

Introduction

Objective → Students will be able to generate equivalent forms of expressions.

Context → This lesson comes early in a unit on writing and solving equations. Students have had experience translating phrases and situations into algebraic symbolism and have learned the properties for addition and multiplication. They will go on to solve linear equations and inequalities.

NCTM Standards Focus

Sometimes students are introduced to simplifying algebraic expressions by jumping straight to the abstract representation and combining like terms. By doing this, students miss seeing the real-world connection to forming and simplifying expressions and how algebraic symbolism can be derived from these situations. In this standards-based lesson, students are able to make that connection. They work with real-world situations and go through a process that enables them to see the value and relevance of writing and simplifying expressions using algebraic symbolism.

Reasoning and Proof Students examine different expressions, formulating their own definitions of like and unlike algebraic terms and creating guidelines for simplifying expressions. They use their own reasoning processes to make the rules for combining terms more meaningful and as a result, become proficient at algebraic manipulations.

Representation Students represent real-world situations algebraically to reinforce their understanding of equivalent expressions and the steps used to simplify an expression. In the process, they recognize that using symbolic forms makes it easier to analyze problems.

Communication Throughout the lesson, students explain their thinking about equivalent expressions and simplification. By sharing ideas, they build on their prior knowledge of mathematical operations to create rules for algebraic work. Group discussion provides a means for students to clarify any points they find difficult or confusing.

Teaching Plan

Materials → Student pages 48–49

BEGIN THE LESSON by grouping students in pairs. Give each student a copy of student page 48. Let students know that they are going to be simplifying expressions and that the worksheet will serve as their guide. Tell students that you do not want them to work ahead but will tell them when they should work on each section of the sheet.

Direct students' attention to the first section, Set A. Explain that for each expression presented in words, they are to first determine whether or not any of the terms in the expression can be combined. Instruct students to simplify each expression, that is, to write an equivalent expression with as few terms as possible by combining all of the like terms. Do not provide students with too much direction at this time, as this is their opportunity to begin formulating their own guidelines for simplifying expressions.

Allow students about 5 minutes to work on the expressions in Set A, then bring them back to a whole group. Have students share their responses and explain the rationale behind simplifying the expressions the way they did. As students share their responses, you may want to pose some or all of the following questions:

- *Which expressions could be rewritten? Why?* (exercises 1–4; they contained some like terms)
- *Which could not be rewritten? Why?* (exercise 5; it contained all unlike terms)
- *What operation did you use for combining like terms?* (addition)
- *When we rearrange the order of the terms, what properties are illustrated?* (commutative and associative properties)

Ask students if they know what property it is that allows like terms to be combined. It is the distributive property, and it can be illustrated using this example from exercise 1:

2 $\times$ apples + 4 $\times$ apples = (2 + 4) apples = 6 apples

Point out that if *apple* were represented as *a*, we could rewrite the sentence as 2a + 4a = (2 + 4)a = 6a.

DIRECT STUDENTS' ATTENTION to Set B. Allow students to work through the expressions, discussing methods and strategies with their peers. Once they have completed Set B, bring them back as a group. Have students share their responses. Pose questions that get students to think about the processes they used.

- *What was similar about the expressions?* (They contained terms that could be rewritten as like terms.)
- *How did you find the like items?* (in exercise 6, finding the Least Common Denominator; in exercises 7 and 8, finding terms that are opposites, such as 9 steps (left) = ⁻9 steps (right) or 2° fall = ⁻2)
- *What operations did you use to combine the terms?* (addition and subtraction)

f.y.i.

Some students may think of *yes* and *no* votes as opposites and combine them to form the equivalent expression of 3 no votes. If so, you might want to engage students in a discussion about combining opposites, or you may wish to postpone the discussion until students finish Set B, in which students must recognize opposites in order to combine terms.

f.y.i.

Students may need to work through more examples of utilizing the distributive property before understanding how to use it in writing expressions. You can create simple examples that demonstrate the use of this property when simplifying expressions.

Direct students' attention to Set C. Allow 5 minutes for students to simplify these expressions. Once they have finished, have students explain the steps they used for each exercise and discuss similarities with earlier examples.

Ask students to suggest a set of steps for simplifying expressions. Typical steps might include rearranging the terms so that like terms are together, then combining like terms by adding or subtracting the coefficients of the like terms.

Now have students examine the expressions in Set D. *Are the steps that you just outlined going to be enough to simplify these expressions?* If not, ask students if they want to change or add to their guidelines or steps. Get them to see they need to apply the distributive property (expand expressions with parentheses first) before rearranging terms. Caution students to be careful about + and − signs when using the distributive property. Have students simplify the expressions in Set D.

What Might Happen . . . What to Do

In exercise 13, students might add the 4 and 5 first, then distribute a factor of 9. Remind students of the order of operations, that multiplication is performed before addition. So $5(2x − 1)$, since it is multiplication, must be done before the 4 is added.

Student Pages

Student page 48 provides students with four sets of expressions. Students simplify the expressions where possible and give reasons why or why not the expression can be simplified. Student page 49 consists of expressions for students to simplify and situations for which students write algebraic expressions.

Assessment

While students simplified expressions on page 48, you observed their understanding of combining like terms. You saw them apply the commutative property to first rearrange, then combine terms. You then assessed their ability to create guidelines or steps for simplifying expressions. When presented with more complicated expressions, you assessed their ability to apply the distributive property prior to rearranging and combining like terms. You also utilized questioning and discussion throughout the lesson as a means for assessing student understanding.

NCTM Standards Summary

In this lesson, students identified the steps involved in simplifying different expressions, then organized the information to formulate some general procedures. By recalling basic properties to justify their work, students recognized that the same rules apply in algebra as in arithmetic problems. This strengthened students' understanding that variables represent numbers. Through the utilization of real-world situations, students compared expressions, identified equivalencies, and kept track of the steps used to simplify expressions. Communication throughout the lesson helped move students toward the goal of creating a set of guidelines for working with expressions.

Answers

Page 48

For 1–8, expressions may vary.

1. Yes; 6 apples + 3 oranges
2. Yes; 12 dimes + 25 pennies
3. Yes; 7 blocks north, 7 blocks east
4. Yes; 31 yes votes, 34 no votes
5. No
6. Yes; $\frac{4}{12} + \frac{3}{12} + \frac{6}{12}$ or $\frac{13}{12}$ or $1\frac{1}{12}$
7. Yes; 6 steps left, 8 steps forward
8. Yes; a rise of 8°
9. Yes; $10m - 5$
10. Yes; $16y + 3x$
11. No
12. Yes; $9c - 9$
13. $10x - 1$
14. $9n - 10$
15. $14y - 9$
16. $19a + 23$

Page 49

1. $6x + 22$
2. $12 - x$
3. ^-8y
4. $^-9x - 3y - 23$
5. $10x - 6y + 41$
6. $24x - 30y - 2$
7. $2x + 2(2x - 1); 6x - 2$
8. $4(x - 2) + 4x + 4(3x + 1);$ $20x - 4$
9. $5x + 12 + 2(3x - 1) + 8x - 6$ $= 19x + 4$

Simplifying Expressions

Can the expression be simplified? Where possible, write the simplified expression.

Set A

① 2 apples + 3 oranges + 4 apples

② 4 dimes + 20 pennies + 8 dimes + 5 pennies

③ A walk of 2 blocks north, 3 blocks east, 5 blocks north, 4 blocks east

④ 6 yes votes, and 15 yes votes and 11 no votes and 10 yes votes and 23 no votes

⑤ 9 hamburgers and 3 pizzas and 12 hot dogs

Set B

⑥ $\frac{1}{3} + \frac{1}{4} + \frac{1}{2}$

⑦ A walk of 2 steps right, 12 steps forward, 9 steps left, 4 steps back, and 1 step right

⑧ A rise of 3°, a fall of 2°, a rise of 10, a rise of 5, and a fall of 8°

Set C

⑨ $4m + 3 + 6m - 8$

⑩ $7y + 8x + 9y - 5x$

⑪ $2x + 3y + 5xy$

⑫ $3 + 2c - 4c - 9 + 11c - 3$

Set D

⑬ $4 + 5(2x - 1)$

⑭ $3(5n - 8) - 2(3n - 7)$

⑮ $9(2y - 3) - 6y + 2(y + 5) + 8$

⑯ $6(3a + 5) - 3 + 5a - (4a - 3) - 7$

Standard 2 Algebra

Simplifying Expressions

Simplify each expression.

1 $7 + 3(2x + 5)$

2 $10 - (6x + 3) + 5(x + 1)$

3 $4(2x - 6y) - 8(x - 2y)$

4 $3 + 2(y + x) - 7(2 + 2x) - 12 + 3x - 5y$

5 $8 - y + 3(2x + 3y) - 7(2y - 5) + 4x - 2$

6 $7x - 3y + 4(2x + y) - 3 + 5(x - 6y) + 4x - y + 1$

Write an algebraic expression that describes each situation. Simplify when possible.

7 The length of a rectangle is 1 foot less than twice its width. Use the fact that $P = 2l + 2w$ to write an expression for the perimeter of the rectangle, then simplify it.

8 The length of a side of one square is 2 cm shorter than the length of a side of a second square. The length of a side of a third square is 1 cm longer than 3 times the length of a side of the second square. Write an expression for the sum of the perimeters of all three squares, then simplify it.

9 Write an expression that describes the perimeter of the figure below, then simplify it.

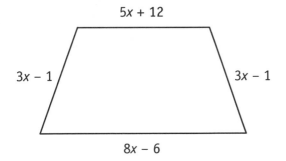

Using Equations

Introduction

Objective → Students will be able to translate a mathematical situation into an equation with a variable and solve it.

Context → Students have had some experience working with variables. They have learned the properties of addition and multiplication, the order of operations, and how to write simple variable expressions. They will go on to solve 1- and 2-step equations.

NCTM Standards Focus

In this standards-based lesson, students are presented with situations that connect to the real world and are asked to translate the situations into symbolic language. As students explore situations that lend themselves to being expressed as equations and as they explore different methods for solving equations, they begin to see the value of using equations as a problem-solving tool. In this lesson, students are engaged in writing and solving 1- and 2-step equations to solve real-world problems.

Representation Students use the symbolism of algebra to represent and analyze real-world situations. They create organized tables, then graph the results to represent the data. Students compare these different representations to better understand the information that can be gained from each.

Communication Students become more fluent with algebraic techniques by explaining the meaning of variables and steps used to translate real-world situations. They communicate strategies used and demonstrate their understanding of how to express different mathematical operations and relationships.

Connections Students connect the process of writing and solving equations to real-world situations, making the process more meaningful to them. They recognize how basic operations are reflected in the equations they write and how properties are applied to solve them. Connecting real-world situations, equations, and graphs helps students see how all three are interrelated.

Teaching Plan

Materials → Student pages 54–55; graph paper

BEGIN THE LESSON by presenting the following situation: *Jason is paid $25.00 per day plus $2.00 for each package he delivers. How much money would Jason earn by delivering 1 package? ($27.00) 2 packages? ($29.00) 5 packages? ($35.00) 20 packages? ($65.00)*

Ask students to explain how they found answers to these questions. *How many operations did you use? What operations? Which operation did you use first?* Ask students to write an equation they could use to find how much Jason would earn for any number of packages. Encourage them to use variables that are easy to associate with the information they represent (i.e., m = money, p = packages).

Have students share their equations and explain why they believe their equations work. If no one suggests the equation $m = 25 + 2p$, offer it your-self. Have students discuss whether or not they could have used this equa-tion to solve the problem. When students realize that the equation could have been used, ask if the amount of money that Jason earns is dependent on the number of packages he delivers. Students should agree that Jason's earnings are dependent on the number of packages delivered. Point out that because the amount of money (m) Jason earns is dependent on the number of packages (p) that he delivers, m is called a *dependent* variable. On the other hand, p is called an *independent* variable. Its value is not dependent on any other value.

GIVE A COPY OF STUDENT PAGE 54 to each student to use as a worksheet during the next part of the lesson. Have students work individu-ally or in pairs to complete the chart at the top of the page. Once they've finished the chart, direct students' attention to the graph on the same page. Explain how the first three points were plotted; then have students com-plete the graph.

When students have completed plotting the points on the graph, point out that the equation, the table, and the graph represent the same situation. Tell them that depending on the situation, one representation of data may be more useful than another. For example, using the equation allows for quick calculation for any number of packages while the graph displays a pattern occurring based on the number of packages delivered. Discuss the relative merits of each form of representation.

Have students carefully examine the graph. *Why does it make sense to use only whole numbers along the horizontal axis of the graph?* (You can't have a fraction of a package.) *As the number of packages increases, what happens to the amount of money?* (It also increases.) *Describe the look of the graph.* (Points seem to be along a straight line.) *Why does the graph look this way?* (Because the increase is constant—always $2.00 per package.)

f.y.i.

As students work through these situations, they won't always represent their equations in the form $y = mx + b$, the general form for linear functions where m is the slope of the line and b is the y-coordinate of the point where the line crosses the y-axis. Do not direct them to do so at this time: rather let them use the variables and equations as a means for solving problems.

Direct students' attention to the situations at the bottom of the page. Again, with students working individually or in pairs, have them create tables and write equations for each situation. If time allows, provide students with a sheet of graph paper and have them construct graphs for the situations presented.

Once students have completed page 54, bring them back together as a group. Encourage them to share their results and the methods used to achieve them. When discussing each situation, have students think about and describe how changes in a situation might affect their equation. *What if the phone company lowered its rate to $0.05 per minute? What if the state fair cut its admission fee in half?* Help students visualize how these types of changes would affect the look of the graph.

HAVE STUDENTS WORK IN PAIRS to create 2–3 real-world problems and write equations that model them. For each situation, ask students to provide as much mathematical information as they can, including whether increasing (decreasing) one variable results in an increase (decrease) in the other variable. Encourage students to represent their equations in both table and graph form. If time allows, have students exchange and solve each other's problems.

What Might Happen . . . What to Do

Some students might still have trouble writing equations with variables. Encourage them to first write out their equation using words, then shorten the equation using the first letter of the key words as their variables.

PASS OUT COPIES of student page 55. Have students work individually or in pairs to complete the problems.

When students have completed the page, take the time to go over their results with the entire class. Have students share the equations they wrote and demonstrate how they are able to use them to solve each problem. Be sure to acknowledge the various approaches and strategies used for successfully solving the problems.

Conclude this lesson by returning to the original situation with Jason delivering packages. Challenge students with a new problem: If Jason earns $91.00 in one day, how many packages did he deliver? (33) Ask students how this problem is different from the original one. Have them discuss the new problem, then share methods they might use to solve this problem.

Student Pages

Student page 54 provides a table and graph for students to record information pertaining to the situation presented to begin the lesson. This page also provides situations for students to represent in both an equation and a table. Student page 55 presents additional problems for students to solve by writing and solving equations.

Assessment

While students responded to questions, wrote and solved equations, and created tables and graphs, you assessed their understanding and fluency with algebraic symbolism. Student-created situations provided indicators of analytical reasoning skills, understanding of basic operations, and the ability to recognize mathematical relationships in a real-world context. You were able to assess how well students transferred these skills and understandings to additional real-world problems.

NCTM Standards Summary

In this lesson, students represented real-world situations using algebraic equations and solving these equations. By doing this, students developed a better understanding of how algebra organizes and simplifies information and relationships. Students were also given the opportunity to compare multiple representations through equations, tables, and graphs. This exercise helped students to recognize how different aspects of mathematics relate to each other. Students used algebra as a method of communicating information in a word description and reinforced their understanding by explaining the steps used to translate the situation into an equation. Connecting this experience to real-world situations enhanced the experience. By emphasizing the connections to basic operations and graphing, this lesson illustrated how mathematical knowledge continually builds on itself.

Answers

Page 54
1. 33, 35, 37, 39, 41, 43
2. Graph should represent data shown in chart.
3–6. Charts and variables used will vary.

Page 55
Student equations will vary.
1. $7.50
2. 12 weeks
3. 7 3-point shots
4. $4.50
5. 40 inches
6. 7 children

Using Equations

❶ Complete the table.

Number of Packages (p)	1	2	3	4	5	6	7	8	9
Money Earned ($m = 25 + 2p$)	27	29	31						

❷ Continue the graph to show the information in Exercise 1.

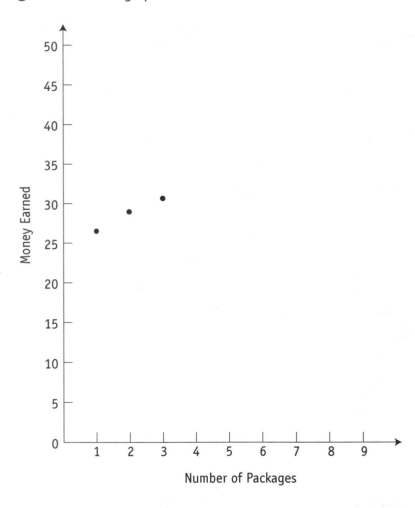

Number of Packages

Create a table and write an equation for each situation.

❸ A long distance phone bill where there is a $5.50 monthly fee and calls cost $0.07 per minute.

❹ Amount of $600.00 prize money remaining if $65 is given away every hour.

❺ Wages for a worker who earns $100.00 per week and $5.00 for every magazine subscription sold.

❻ Cost of a trip to the state fair with $10.00 admission fee and a charge of $1.50 per ride.

Standard 2 Algebra

Using Equations

Write an equation for each problem. Solve your equations.

① Camille raised $60 by selling 8 coupon books for her school fundraiser. How much do the coupon books cost?

② Kaina has $36 dollars saved. He figures he needs $120 (tax included) to buy the new skateboard he's had his eye on. If he puts away $7 of his allowance each week, how long will it be before he has enough money for the skateboard?

③ Iliana was the star of the basketball game. She scored only 8 points in the first half but hit all 3-point shots in the second half to wind up with 29 points. How many 3-point shots did she make in the second half of the game?

④ Courtney painted her neighbor's fence, earning $22.50 for 5 hours of work. How much did Courtney earn per hour of work?

Use variables and equations to solve each problem.

⑤ The length of a rectangle is three times the width. If the width is 5 inches, what is the perimeter of the rectangle?

⑥ A group of neighbors went to a pancake breakfast and spent a total of $46.25. The cost for adults was $4.50; the cost for children was $2.75. There were 6 adults in the group. How many children went to the breakfast?

Analyzing Patterns

Introduction

Objective → Students will solve problems by identifying and continuing a pattern.

Context → Students have worked with patterns and have described rules verbally. They have had experience in translating words into algebraic expressions and evaluating formulas. Subsequent lessons may cover sums of finite arithmetic and geometric sequences.

NCTM Standards Focus

In this standards-based lesson, reasoning and representation are important in helping students develop strategies to identify and describe patterns. Students represent the same patterns in a variety of ways, including verbal, numerical, algebraic, and geometric and so gain insight into the relationships that exist. A problem-solving approach enables students to see how discerning the rules for patterns can be a valuable problem-solving tool.

Reasoning and Proof Students use reasoning to determine whether a set of numbers or figures represents a pattern. They compare different types of patterns, develop their own methods for analyzing patterns, and generalize information about patterns. Students justify their thinking by showing how their solutions conform to the pattern identified.

Representation By examining patterns represented by geometric models and in table form, students recognize that the same pattern can be described differently and gain insight into how the numbers can be represented algebraically. They also recognize that one form of representation may be more useful than another.

Problem Solving Students have the opportunity to use patterns to solve real-world problems. As they analyze and use patterns, it will become clear that this strategy provides a shortcut that can minimize tedious calculation.

Teaching Plan

Materials → Student pages 60–61; graph paper

BEGIN THE LESSON by presenting a simple problem to engage students in examining situations that involve patterns.

A botanist kept track of the number of leaves that grew on a plant he was studying. The table shows information he recorded.

Day	1	2	3	4	5	6
Number of Leaves	2	4	6	8	10	12

Do you see a pattern in the way the leaves grow? What different ways can you think of to describe this pattern? (The numbers representing the leaves

are the multiples of 2; each day, the number of leaves increases by 2.)
Predict the number of leaves for the next two days. (14, 16)

Point out that patterns can often be represented geometrically. Have students work individually or in pairs to draw a geometric representation of the pattern for leaf growth on graph paper. Then have students compare their work. Most students will show stacks of squares or dots.

ASK STUDENTS HOW this same pattern could be expressed using a formula or equation. Students will most likely offer some form of the sentence $n = 2d$, where n represents the number of leaves and d represents the number of days. *If the pattern continues, how many leaves will there be on the 10th day?* (20) *On the 25th day?* (50) Discuss the advantages of using a formula like this.

PRESENT ANOTHER PROBLEM for students to work on.

Gino just opened a pizza restaurant. He had 2 customers the first day, 4 the second day, 7 the third day, and 11 the fourth day. If this pattern continues, how many customers should Gino expect on the seventh day?

Suggest that students represent the information in a table.

Day	1	2	3	4
Number of Customers	2	4	7	11

Ask students how this pattern is similar to, and different from, the previous one. Suggest they represent this pattern on graph paper by shading stacks of squares. Some students will gain insight from the numerical representation; for others, the drawing will be more meaningful. Ask students to identify the rule for this pattern. Engage students in a discussion of the strategies they used to find the pattern as they describe their rule.

Methods Students Might Use

- Consider the differences between successive terms. There is a difference of 2 between the first two terms, and the difference increases by 1 for each successive term. The numbers that result from continuing these differences through the seventh day are 2, 4, 7, 11, 16, 22, and 29, so there will be 29 customers on the seventh day.

- Relate the number of customers, or term, to the day, or term number.

On Day 1, the number of customers was one greater than the number of the day and there were two customers. On Day 2, the number of customers increased by two (the number of customers of the previous day), yielding four customers. On Day 3 the number of customers increased by four, and so on.

The rule can be described as *the number of customers for any day equals number of customers on the previous day, plus the number of the day,* or, *the number of customers equals the term number plus the term for the previous term number.* This can be expressed as $n = d + p$, where n represents the number of customers and d represents the number of the day, and p represents the number of customers on the previous day.

Point out that with either method it is necessary to compute a number for each of the previous days in order to find the customers for Day 7. Ask students to decide which of the following formulas describes the pattern they just explored and to use that formula to find the number of customers; c, on Day 12, using n to represent day number.

a. $c = n(n + 1)$ b. $c = 1 + \frac{n(n + 1)}{2}$ c. $c = n + 2(n + 1)$

Have students discuss their solutions and ask them to explain the method(s) they used. (b; 79 customers on Day 12. Students should explain that they substituted 12 for n and computed.) *How can you check this answer?* (By using the pattern rule to write out all the numbers through Day 12)

AS A FINAL ACTIVITY, present a problem that involves multiplication.

Lea saved 5¢ on the first day of the month, 10¢ on the second day, 20¢ on the third day, and so on. How much money will Lea save on the ninth day of the month? At the end of the ninth day, how much money will she have saved in all? ($12.80 on the ninth day; total $25.55)

Have students work in pairs to identify the pattern and the rule and answer both questions. Encourage them to share the thinking they used to analyze the pattern as they discuss the solutions. *Do you think one method is easier to use than others? Did anyone find a formula?* ($s = 5 \times 2^{n-1}$; where s represents savings on a particular day and n represents the number of the day.)

f.y.i.

You may wish to mention that there is a method (the method of finite differences) for finding a formula for this type of pattern, and that students will learn it in later algebra courses.

Student Pages

Student page 60 provides patterns for students to explore. Student page 61 presents application problems.

Assessment

There were opportunities to assess students' understanding of pattern rules and representations as they made tables and drawings and responded during class discussions. Students' success with exercises on the student pages also served as indicators of their proficiency with the concepts and methods involving patterning.

NCTM Standards Summary

Reasoning was a central focus of this lesson as students developed their own strategies for identifying and describing patterns. This approach made the fact that there are different ways to solve a problem apparent. Students used verbal, numerical, algebraic, and geometric representations of patterns as they created alternative modes by which they could gain insight into a problem. Recognizing patterns as a problem-solving tool that can be applied to a variety of situations provided the underlying rationale for the lesson.

Answers

Page 60

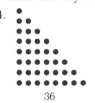

1. ⋮ 15

2. ⋮ 21   ⋮ 28

3. Answers may vary.

4. ⋮ 36

5. $\dfrac{n(n+1)}{2}$ 6. 210

7.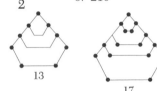
13   17

8. The numbers increase by 4.

9. 21, 25, 29

10. $4n - 3$ 11. 57

Page 61

1. $-5, -7, -9$

2. $\dfrac{6}{7}, \dfrac{7}{8}, \dfrac{8}{9}$

3. 27, 32, 37

4. $\dfrac{1}{243}, \dfrac{1}{729}, \dfrac{1}{2187}$

5. $64, -128, 256$

6. 15; 13; 169

7. 560 students

8. 125 gallons

9. $259; $400;

Differences must be found on three levels. Find differences between the first set of terms, and then find the differences between the numbers you get. The second set of differences is increasing by 6. To get the next two pattern numbers, work backward; add 6 to the last term of the second set of differences, then add that to the term for the 5th day. Repeat the procedure.

Analyzing Patterns

Use the triangular numbers below to answer questions 1–6.

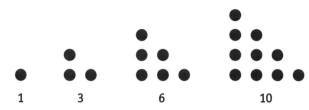

1   3   6   10

❶ Draw the next triangular number.
a. What is the number?

❸ Describe the pattern for triangular numbers.

❺ Which formula describes the nth triangular number?

  a. $\dfrac{n(n+1)}{2}$ b. $n(n-1)+2$

❷ Find the next two triangular numbers by drawing the dot pictures. What are the numbers?

❹ Predict the next triangular number. Check your prediction by drawing the dot picture.

❻ Use the formula to find the 20th triangular number.

Use the pentagonal numbers below to answer questions 7–11.

❼ Make drawings to find the next two pentagonal numbers.

❾ Predict the next three pentagonal numbers.

⓫ Use the formula to find the 15th pentagonal number.

❽ Describe the pattern for these pentagonal numbers.

❿ Which formula describes the nth pentagonal number?

  a. $4(n+1)$ b. $4n-3$

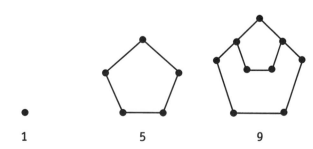

1   5   9

Analyzing Patterns

Find the next three terms of each pattern.

1 5, 3, 1, ⁻1, ⁻3, . . .

2 $\frac{1}{2}, \frac{2}{3}, \frac{3}{4}, \frac{4}{5}, \frac{5}{6}, \ldots$

3 2, 7, 12, 17, 22, . . .

4 $1, \frac{1}{3}, \frac{1}{9}, \frac{1}{27}, \frac{1}{81}, \ldots$

5 ⁻2, 4, ⁻8, 16, ⁻32, . . .

Solve each problem.

6 A display in a grocery store has soup cans stacked with 25 cans in the bottom row, 23 cans in the second row from the bottom, 21 cans in the third row from the bottom, and so on.
  a. How many soup cans are in the sixth row from the bottom?
  b. What is the maximum number of rows possible in the display?
  c. What is the maximum number of cans possible in the display?

Year	1997	1998	1999	2000
Students	1000	980	950	910

7 The table shows the freshman class enrollment at Math University.
If the pattern continues, how many students will be in the freshman class of 2005?

8 A tank contains 16,000 gallons of oil. Each day, one-half of the oil in the tank is used and not replaced. How much oil is left in the tank at the end of the seventh day?

9 **Challenge:** Phil is trying to figure out what method his boss uses to pay him. The first week he worked, Phil was paid only $4. The next week he was paid $15, then $40, then $85, and then $156. Determine how much Phil will be paid for each of the next two weeks? Explain your method.

Translating Algebraic Expressions

Introduction

Objective → Students will translate phrases into algebraic expressions for the four basic operations.

Context → Students have had experience evaluating expressions. They will go on to distinguish between expressions, equations, and statements of inequality and translate word problems into complete sentences to be solved.

Translating Algebraic Expressions

Learn

You can take a written or spoken mathematical expression and translate it into symbols.

For example, *a number multiplied by 8* can be translated to $n \times 8$.

Here are some other examples.

Sixteen less than 20 can be written as $20 - 16$.

Five times a number can be written as $5n$.

Four greater than a number can be written as $4 + n$.

Half of a number can be written as $\frac{1}{2} \times n$ or $\frac{n}{2}$.

Triple a number can be written as $3n$.

Three times twice a number can be written as $3 \times 2n$.

Explore

Does *a number decreased by* 3 mean the same as *three less than a number*? Explain.

Try

Write the following mathematical expressions in symbols.

1. a number minus nine
2. five divided by a number
3. two more than a number
4. six times a number
5. six less than a number
6. one more than two times a number
7. a number plus ten
8. a number divided by 6

NCTM Process Standards Analysis and Focus

The standards analysis examines how the process standards have been incorporated into the above lesson. By increasing the focus on three of the process standards, a more effective and meaningful lesson can be presented. The suggestions offered can help you to think about how this might be accomplished.

Connections The lesson connects word phrases with symbolic notation, but the concept is not fully developed. Limited attention is given to the vocabulary connected with the operations.

Suggestion → Encourage students to recall prior knowledge about how mathematical relationships are described to compile a list of various ways the four operations can be expressed. Making

Practice

Match each word expression with its symbolic expression.

1.	$n + 4$	a)	one-fourth of a number
2.	$4n$	b)	four added to a number
3.	$\frac{1}{4}n$	c)	a number multiplied by four
4.	$4 - n$	d)	four subtracted from a number
5.	$4 \div n$	e)	a number subtracted from four
6.	$n - 4$	f)	four divided by a number

Write each of the following word expressions in symbols.

7.	a number increased by one-half	10.	a number decreased by two-thirds
8.	a number increased by eighteen	11.	four less than a number
9.	twelve divided by a number	12.	eight times a number

Problem Solving

Let b be the number of books sold last week. Write a symbolic expression for each word expression. Use the expression to answer each question.

13. Suzanne sold twenty fewer books this week than she sold last week.
   Question: If she sold seventy-five books last week, how many did she sell this week?

14. Ken sold twelve more books this week than he did last week.
   Question: If he sold fifty-three books last week, how many did he sell this week?

15. Jason sold twice as many books this week as he did last week.
   Question: If he sold thirty-five books last week, how many did he sell this week?

16. Peggy sold a third as many books this week as she sold last week.
   Question: If she sold sixty books last week, how many did she sell this week?

such a list will help students become aware of the variety of phrases that can correspond to the same algebraic expression.

Communication Students are asked to write expressions for phrases, however, the lesson offers minimal opportunity for students to discuss their work and comment on important ideas.

Suggestion → Have students collaborate as they compile phrases representing numerical relationships. Instruct them to create the most comprehensive list of phrases possible. Having opportunities to discuss different ways that numerical relationships can be stated will increase students' understanding of algebraic expressions.

Reasoning and Proof Exercises and questions that require students to reason or generalize are not included in this lesson.

Suggestion → To help them understand the importance of order in writing certain expressions, direct students to check their expressions using the commutative property. Encourage students to develop their own methods of determining whether their translations are correct. Demonstrate using numerical substitution to check expressions. These activities will increase understanding of the relationship between algebra and arithmetic.

Problem Solving Exercises labeled problem solving are actually sentences that contain word phrases to be translated into mathematical expressions.

Representation Algebraic representations of word phrases are presented with minimal explanation.

f.y.i.

Statements of inequality such as
$3 + m > 12$ or $5y < 18$ are also
complete sentences that contain
expressions.

The teaching plan that follows shows how the suggestions for increasing the focus on the process standards can be implemented.

Revised Teaching Plan

BEGIN THE LESSON BY EXPLAINING that mathematical expressions use numbers, letters, and operation or relating signs to represent word phrases that describe numerical relationships. Mathematical expressions by themselves do not express a complete thought, but they may be part of a complete sentence. Being able to translate word phrases into mathematical expressions is important in both problem solving and algebra.

HELP STUDENTS DISTINGUISH between a complete sentence in the form of an equation and an expression. You might relate this difference to distinguishing between a phrase and a complete sentence in English. *If I said "next Tuesday" you would have some information, but would you know what I meant about next Tuesday? "Next Tuesday" is an example of a phrase. Note the difference when I say, "The game is next Tuesday." Adding information to a phrase can make it a complete thought. In mathematics, an expression is a phrase that describes a mathematical relationship; the complete thought is a math sentence.*

Write *3 years older than Jorge* on the board. *Is this a complete thought or a phrase?* (phrase.) *Does this phrase describe a mathematical relationship?* (yes.) *How could we represent this phrase mathematically?* (J + 3 or 3 + J) *J + 3 is an example of a mathematical expression. A complete sentence might be "Donna is 3 years older than Jorge." How would we represent that complete thought mathematically?* (D = J + 3) *Adding information has changed this mathematical expression into an equation. In this lesson, we will be concentrating on expressions.*

HAVE STUDENTS WORK IN GROUPS to compile lists of all the phrases they can think of to express addition, subtraction, multiplication, and division. Then ask them to write mathematical expressions for their phrases. This exercise will create awareness that different word phrases may have the same mathematical expression. By making connections to their prior knowledge about the operations and communicating their ideas with one another, students will review and extend their translation skills.

Typical possibilities might include:

Addition

a number plus 10	$n + 10$
6 increased by a number	$6 + n$
7 more than a number	$n + 7$
15 and n more	$15 + n$

Subtraction

a number minus 5	$n - 5$
the difference between a number and 8	$n - 8$
3 less than a number	$n - 3$
12 reduced by n	$12 - n$

Multiplication

4 times a number	$4n$
the product of 9 and a number	$9n$
a number multiplied by 5	$5n$
half of a number	$\frac{1}{2}n$

Division

a number divided by 6	$\frac{n}{6}$ or $n \div 6$
the quotient of 100 and a number	$100 \div n$ or $\frac{100}{n}$
a number divided by 50	$n \div 50$ or $\frac{n}{50}$
24 divided by n	$\frac{24}{n}$ or $24 \div n$

f.y.i.

Students may associate *half of a number* **with division, dividing the number by 2 and taking one of the two equal portions. However, students should be made aware that half of a number is also the number multiplied by the fraction $\frac{1}{2}$.**

After students have had time to complete their lists, ask groups to share their ideas. Compile a list for the entire class on the board. Encourage students to discuss suggestions and indicate whether they agree that their expressions are correct. Be sure that all four operations receive adequate entries.

NEXT, ASK QUESTIONS THAT GIVE STUDENTS an opportunity to communicate the reasoning they used to write different expressions. *When translating a phrase, do you always write the terms in the order in which they are given?* (No.) *Give an example.* (5 less than a number is written $n - 5$, not $5 - n$.) *How can you show that* n − 5 *and* 5 − n *do not mean the same thing?* Demonstrate substituting a numerical value for the letter. For example, if n equals 9, substitution will show that $9 - 5$ is 4, but $5 - 9$ is ⁻4. Using substitution will help students see that the correct expression for "5 less than a number" is $n - 5$. This discussion focuses students' thinking on meaning rather than on making a mechanical translation and helps them develop a tool for checking their work.

What Might Happen . . . What to Do

Students may have difficulty identifying the quantity to represent with a letter or with choosing the operation. Discuss strategies such as visualizing the situation or using substitution. To translate "20 pounds more than the carton's weight,"

- Draw a cube to represent a carton and add 20. (cube + 20) Replace the cube with a variable. (c + 20)

- Try substituting different values to represent the unknown amount. For example, if the carton weighs 10 pounds, you would have 10 + 20. If the carton weighs 20 pounds, you would have 20 + 20. If the carton weighs c pounds, you would have c + 20.

Ask students which types of expressions require the most thought to translate and why. Students will probably identify those involving subtraction and division. Connect to prior learning about the commutative property by asking students to explain why the order of the terms matters for subtraction and division but not for addition and multiplication. This type of reasoning and communication helps students gain a better understanding of relationships that exist between arithmetic and algebra and will stimulate them to think more critically about their work.

CONCLUDE BY REMINDING STUDENTS that this lesson began with their translating word phrases into mathematical expressions. Inform them that the lesson will end with your giving them several mathematical expressions to translate into word phrases. Start with the expressions here and instruct students to make as many phrases as they can for each.

$3 + y$	$n - 12$
3 plus a number	a number minus 12
y more than 3	12 less than a number
3 increased by y	12 subtracted from a number
3 and y more	a number decreased by 12

$2\frac{2}{3}n$	$\frac{y}{9}$
$2\frac{2}{3}n$ times a number	a number divided by 9
a number multiplied by $2\frac{2}{3}$	the quotient of y and 9

Extension

You might extend learning by having students translate more complex phrases such as "the product of 5 and a number, decreased by 2." Explain how the comma is used to prevent misreading, so it is clear the phrase means $5n - 2$ and not $5(n - 2)$. Also consider having students translate statements of inequality.

Student Pages

Students should now be ready to complete excercises similar to those on the reduced student pages.

Assessment

Observing students as they compiled their lists and participated in class discussion provided opportunities to assess their understanding of how to translate phrases. Students' skills could also be evaluated as they responded to the oral exercises at the close of the lesson.

NCTM Standards Summary

Students gained a better understanding of the connection between a word phrase and a mathematical expression by compiling their own lists of phrases and translating them to expressions. The opportunities for reasoning and communication throughout the lesson enabled students to explore the meanings of their expressions and develop ways to determine if their work was correct. Because they were asked to explain their thinking and make connections to what they already knew about the basic operations, students could see the close relationship between arithmetic and algebra.

Standard 3 **Geometry**

A T T H E S E V E N T H G R A D E L E V E L, geometry
includes work with transformations, representing two- and
three-dimensional shapes, congruence and similarity, and properties
of plane figures. Our lessons are derived from these important
topics, and include a lesson on exploring transformations, a lesson
on representing views of three-dimensional shapes, a lesson that
analyzes transformations and congruence, and a lesson on the angle-
sum relationships of triangles and quadrilaterals.

Three lessons model how the process standards can be used to
teach content. A fourth lesson is a hypothetical textbook lesson that
we have revised to be more standards based. These four lessons
do not represent the entire curriculum, but rather provide glimpses
of how, with a more concentrated effort to incorporate the process
standards, better mathematics teaching and learning can be achieved.

One lesson we have chosen explores the reflections of figures on
a coordinate plane. Reasoning and proof is the main process standard that motivates this lesson as students look for patterns in the
coordinates of figures and their reflections in order to predict the
coordinates of other reflected figures.

Another lesson we have chosen is one in which students draw two-dimensional views of three-dimensional figures. The process standards of representation, problem solving, and communication drive this lesson that asks students to think about what information must be known so that a figure may be reconstructed.

A third lesson we have chosen is one in which students describe transformations that could be used to move a geometric figure onto a congruent figure. By incorporating the process standards of representation, reasoning and proof, and communication, students look for patterns in the coordinates of the vertices of congruent figures. Students write rules to describe the transformations, and try to express them algebraically.

The hypothetical textbook lesson we have chosen to revise is a lesson that explores the sums of the measures of the angles of triangles and quadrilaterals. Through better incorporation of the process standards of connections, reasoning and proof, and representation, students see how the 180° in a straight angle becomes the 180° in a triangle, and how a quadrilateral can be divided into two triangles. This is important because this method leads to finding the sum of the measures of the angles of polygons with more sides.

Standard 3 Lessons

Exploring Transformations

Representing Views of Three-Dimensional Shapes

Analyzing Transformation and Congruence

Investigating Angle-Sum Relationships

Exploring Transformations

Introduction

Objective → Students will explore reflections of two-dimensional shapes on a coordinate grid and describe the shapes according to their coordinates and quadrants.

Context → In earlier lessons students have plotted points on a coordinate plane and they have identified translations and reflections of two-dimensional shapes. In future lessons students use transformations to prove similarity and congruence.

NCTM Standards Focus

This lesson calls on students to make a conjecture about reflected shapes on a coordinate plane, then challenges them to use the coordinates to verify their conjectures. Students use diagrams and sets of coordinate pairs to represent the shapes. The use of coordinate grids to show reflected figures extends the lesson beyond the traditional method of teaching similar figures.

Reasoning and Proof Students find patterns in sets of coordinate pairs that describe reflected figures, and verify that the patterns hold by plotting the points and drawing the figures.

Representation Students represent reflected figures with sets of coordinate pairs and draw the figures by plotting the points.

Communication Students use the coordinate grid system to communicate the reflections and predict the reflected figure.

Teaching Plan

Materials → Student pages 74–75; straightedges; grid paper

BEGIN THE LESSON with a general discussion about reflections. *What is a reflection?* (An image given back by a surface such as a mirror.) *How does a reflection differ from the original?* (The image is reversed side to side—for example, something on the left side of the original will be on the right side of the reflection.)

Draw a triangle on the board. Discuss how you might make a reflection of it. To help students visualize the reflection, have them imagine a mirror held up to the image. Students may suggest that to make a reflection, you "flip" the shape, anchoring it at one point or along one side.

Distribute student page 74. Go over with students how the four quadrants in a coordinate grid are labeled. The upper right quadrant, described by positive numbers on both the *x*-axis and *y*-axis, is quadrant I. The upper left quadrant (negative *x*, positive *y*) is quadrant II. The lower left quadrant (negative *x*, negative *y*) is quadrant III. The lower right quadrant (positive *x*, negative *y*) is quadrant IV.

Point out the first table of coordinates on page 74. Have students predict in which quadrant the shape will fall and why. (Quadrant II; the points are all negative x and positive y.) Give students time to plot the points and connect them with line segments to form the triangle.

Challenge students to make a reflection of the triangle, placing the reflection in quadrant I. Allow them to use any strategy they wish. Point out that the reflection must be the same size and shape as the original triangle, but it should be flipped so that it is a mirror image of the first triangle. Give students some time to make their reflections.

What Might Happen . . . What to Do

Some students might have difficulty understanding how a reflection relates to the original figure and might draw a simple translation. Use grid paper on the overhead to help students see this concept. Draw a horizontal and vertical axis; then draw a triangle in quadrant II. Ask students to imagine that the y-axis is a mirror.

What would the triangle look like reflected in that mirror? Have them imagine laying that triangle flat in quadrant I as you draw the reflection in quadrant I. Repeat this a few times. Using triangles with exaggerated shapes can help students understand the relationship between the original and the flipped image.

Ask students to look at their original triangle and reflected triangle. *Are the two figures mirror images? How can you tell?* Students should notice that the point closest to the y-axis on the original triangle corresponds to the point closest to the y-axis on the reflection. The points farthest from the y-axis on both triangles also correspond to each other. *If you didn't have a mirror image and instead slid the triangle from quadrant I to quadrant II, what would you have?* (Two identical triangles in which the two left sides correspond and the two right sides correspond)

Have volunteers describe how they drew the triangle's reflection. Many students may have drawn the reflection without referring to the coordinates. If no one made the reflection by adjusting the given coordinates, ask the

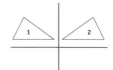

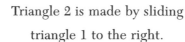

Triangle 2 is made by sliding
triangle 1 to the right.

Triangle 2 is a reflection of
triangle 1.

class to report the coordinates for the reflected triangle as you record them.
[(5, 5), (5, 1), (3, 3)] *How do these coordinates compare to the original coordinates?* (The *x*-coordinates are opposite.)

WRITE THE COORDINATES for problem 2 on the board. *In which quadrant would these points fall? How do you know?* (Quadrant IV; the *x*-coordinates are positive and the *y*-coordinates are negative.) Have students graph the points, then connect them to form a shape. *What kind of shape do you have?* (An irregular five-sided polygon)

Suppose you make a reflection of this figure in quadrant I. Note that this time, students can imagine that there is a mirror along the *x*-axis in which the figure is reflected. *How will this reflection be similar to and different from the reflection from quadrant II to quadrant I?* (The points closest to the *x*-axis and the points farthest from the *x*-axis will correspond to each other. The original figure will be reflected over a horizontal line rather than a vertical line.)

Have students explain how they could use the coordinates for the original figure in quadrant IV to find the coordinates of the reflection in quadrant I. (Change the *y*-coordinates from negative to positive.) Have students fill in the blank table with the coordinates for the reflection. Then have them plot the points they have written and use them to draw the reflection of the shape in quadrant I. *Did your method of finding the coordinates for the reflection work?*

CHALLENGE STUDENTS TO MAKE another reflection of the original figure, this time in quadrant III. Again have them list the coordinates for the reflection before drawing the figure. *How did you change the coordinates for the original figure in quadrant IV to make the reflection in quadrant III?* (Change the *x*-coordinates from positive to negative.)

Now have students look at the reflections in quadrant III and quadrant I. *Are these two figures reflections of each other? Why?* Students should see that they are reflections and that both the x- and y-coordinates are opposites of each other.

Now have students work with a partner. Have each student draw a figure in a quadrant and exchange it with a friend and challenge them to make a reflection. Have students make different figures and make reflections in different ways.

Review how to make a reflection of a figure in a different quadrant on a coordinate grid. Then give students page 75 for either work in class or homework. Students draw a polygon of their choice in quadrant I and list its coordinates. Then have them list coordinates for that figure's reflection in each of the other three quadrants. Finally, they should check their work by using their coordinates to draw the three reflections.

Student Pages

Student page 74 is for use with the in-class activity. Student page 75 provides a larger blank coordinate grid and space for students to record the coordinates for an original figure in quadrant I and reflections of the figure in each of the other three quadrants.

Assessment

You had an opportunity to determine whether students understood reflections from one quadrant to another as you did the activity on page 74 in class. When students worked with a partner you had another opportunity to gauge their understanding of reflections on a grid. Finally, the student page gave you a chance to look at students' individual work.

NCTM Standards Summary

Students used reasoning to find a relationship between the coordinates of reflected shapes on a coordinate plane. They verified their ideas by using the relationship to determine coordinates for the reflections of given figures. Then using those coordinates, they drew the figures to confirm that they were reflections of the original.

Answers

Page 74
1. Check student drawings for accuracy.
2. A. Check students' graphs.
   B. (5, 2), (3, 4), (5, 5), (2, 7), (2, 2)
   C. ($^-$5, $^-$2), ($^-$3, $^-$4), ($^-$5, $^-$5), ($^-$2, $^-$7), ($^-$2, $^-$2)

Page 75
Answers will vary. Check student drawings for accuracy.

Exploring Transformations

Follow the directions for each coordinate grid below.

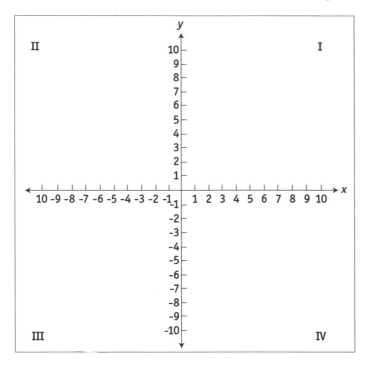

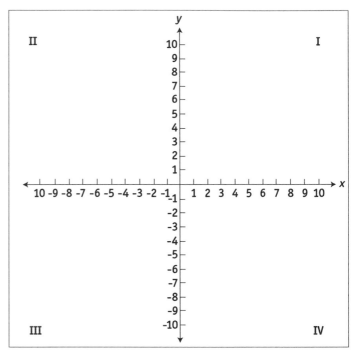

❶ Plot these points on the grid. Connect the points to form a figure. Then draw a reflection of the figure in quadrant I.

x	y
⁻5	5
⁻5	1
⁻3	3

❷ A. Plot these points on the grid. Connect the points as you plot them.

x	y
5	⁻2
3	⁻4
5	⁻5
2	⁻7
2	⁻2

B. Make a reflection of this figure in quadrant I. Record the coordinates for the reflection in the table. Plot the points for the reflection.

x	y

C. Make a reflection of this figure in quadrant III. Record the coordinates for the reflection in the table. Plot the points for the reflection.

x	y

Standard 3 Geometry

Exploring Transformations

List the coordinates for a figure of your choice in quadrant I. Then list the coordinates for reflections of the figure in the other quadrants. Finally, plot the coordinates. Draw the figure and its reflections.

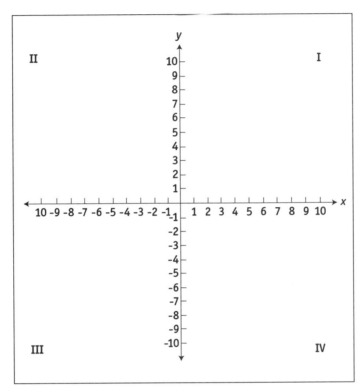

Quadrant I		Quadrant II		Quadrant III		Quadrant IV	
x	*y*	*x*	*y*	*x*	*y*	*x*	*y*

Representing Views of Three-Dimensional Shapes

Introduction

Objective → Students will draw two-dimensional views of three-dimensional models. They will make drawings that provide the information necessary to reconstruct models.

Context → This lesson comes midway through a unit on surface area and volume. Students have identified various solid figures and have practiced drawing them in two- and three-dimensions. They have worked with surface area and will go on to determine volumes.

NCTM Standards Focus

Making two-dimensional representations of three-dimensional models will develop students' visual reasoning skills and help them analyze part/whole relationships of solid figures. Reconstructing models from two-dimensional drawings will affirm and reinforce understanding.

Representation Students will make two-dimensional drawings to represent different views of three-dimensional figures constructed from cubes. They will evaluate drawings to determine whether they uniquely characterize models, and they will extend representations to include all information necessary to reconstruct models.

Reasoning and Proof Reasoning will be activated as students determine how to create two-dimensional drawings of figures and predict which two-dimensional drawings are needed to reconstruct models. Students will explain their reasoning and will validate their predications by reconstructing figures from their drawings.

Communication Students will discuss aspects of models to determine features that must be included in drawings. As students discuss what should be included in different views, they will clarify and strengthen their visual understanding of these forms.

Teaching Plan

Materials → Student pages 80–81; about 36 connecting cubes per student; grid paper

Preparation → Construct models for Figures 1, 2, 3, and 4 before the lesson.

ASK STUDENTS IF THEY CAN THINK OF any situations when a three-dimensional figure is represented in two dimensions. Possibilities might include perspective drawings, architects' plans, or cross-sectional drawings of component parts. *What is the difference between a perspective rendering of a building (as in a painting) and an architect's plans? For what purposes might an architect use each of these types of rendering?* (Architects use three-dimensional renderings of buildings—usually in watercolor and or pencil—to show how buildings look in space, that is, how they look to the eye. Architects use plans to show how buildings actually exist in space with layout and dimensions.) *Which would be more useful for building the* structure, *a three-dimensional drawing or plans?* (The plans. The three-dimensional representation shows how the building actually looks, but plans show the exact proportions of the building and usually the scale, so the building can be replicated without the architect being present.)

Figure 1

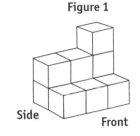

TO PREPARE STUDENTS TO MAKE their own two-dimensional drawings, distribute cubes and grid paper. Display the prepared model of Figure 1 and identify the front and side views. Make a three-dimensional drawing of Figure 1 on the board. Then ask volunteers to draw two-dimensional views of the front and side on the board. Make sure students understand that a two-dimensional view is a straight-on view that does not use perspective. Discuss differences among the model, the three-dimensional drawing, and the two-dimensional views.

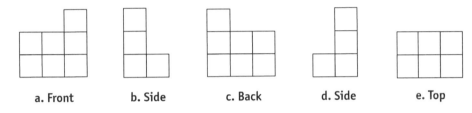

| a. Front | b. Side | c. Back | d. Side | e. Top |

Have students draw front, back, side, and top views of the model on grid paper and share their drawings. *If you were going to reconstruct a model of Figure 1 from cubes using just drawings, which views would be needed?* (At least two views, a side plus either front or back, would be needed.) Ask students to construct models of Figure 1 from their drawings. *Were the views you predicted were needed the ones that you used to construct your model?*

DISPLAY THE MODEL OF FIGURE 2 and draw Figure 2 on the board. Identify the front and side views and ask students to make two-dimensional drawings of front, side, and top views on their graph paper. Have students share their drawings. *Which views would be needed to reconstruct this model with cubes?* Students should point out that they cannot reconstruct this model from drawings unless they have a top view, either a front or back view, and one side view. As before, have students construct the model from their drawings.

Figure 2

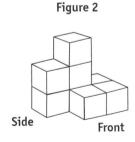

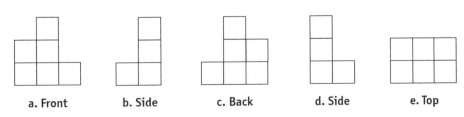

| a. Front | b. Side | c. Back | d. Side | e. Top |

Figure 3

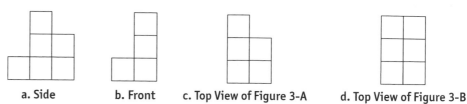

Side

Front

3-A

Side

Front

3-B

DRAW THE TWO MODELS SHOWN in Figure 3 on the board. Identify the front and side of each figure and ask students to draw front and side views. Some students may be confused by the drawings of Figure 3. If so, have them try to build the two figures to focus on the differences in the two models. Ask students to describe similarities and differences in their two drawings. Although the models are different, the front and side views are the same.

a. Side   b. Front   c. Top View of Figure 3-A   d. Top View of Figure 3-B

Discuss how front and side views alone do not provide enough information about how cubes are stacked and that front cubes may obstruct parts of the model. Encourage students to verbalize this problem. Ask them what would be needed to make the difference between the two more clear. Students should suggest showing a top view. Have them draw top views of Figure 3-A and 3-B.

1	
1	3
1	2

1	1
1	3
1	2

Top views of 3-A and 3-B
with numbers added

Explain that the top view and what would be a bottom view, or a base-layer view, are essentially the same. Ask students to consider how showing the number of cubes that are in each stack of the top/base-layer views would make the distinctions between Figures 3-A and 3-B even clearer. Demonstrate how to count and add numbers to a top/base-layer view to represent the number of cubes in each stack.

Figure 4

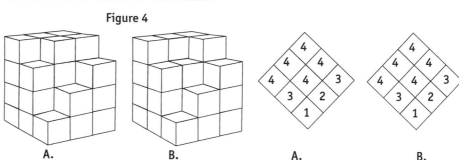

A.   B.   A.   B.

Now, show students the two models for Figure 4. Ask volunteers to make base-layer drawings with numbers on the board for the two models. Reinforce how the drawings show the difference between the models.

CONCLUDE THE LESSON by having individuals or pairs build their own models and then complete their own base-layer drawings of those models. When you feel students are ready, encourage them to construct a more

complex cube model and make a base-layer drawing for their model.
Tell them to remove their model from view and exchange drawings with
another student. Students should reconstruct each other's models from the
base-layer drawings and then compare their result with the original figure.
Instruct students to draw front and side views after construction and
have them refine their drawings as needed. Student pages may be used as
additional class work or as homework.

Student Pages

Student page 80 provides practice in identifying and drawing front and
side views of three-dimensional models. Student page 81 provides students
with an opportunity to identify and create drawings and illustrate three-
dimensional models from given base-level drawings.

Assessment

Responses during class discussions provided ample opportunity to assess
students' ability to analyze models. Drawing activities provided good indicators of students' visualization skills. By observing their work as they created
base-layer drawings and built models, you could evaluate students' understanding of the concepts in this lesson.

NCTM Standards Summary

By reasoning through how to represent three-dimensional models using two-
dimensional views, students developed an understanding of the elements
required to create representations with this method. Throughout the lesson,
students reasoned about how to translate one representation to another,
explained how they arrived at their drawings, and checked their results by
reconstructing models. Their explanations affirmed and reinforced their
visualization skills.

Answers

Page 80

1. c

2. c

3.

Front   Side

4.

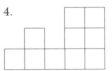 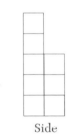

Front   Side

5.

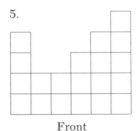

Front   Side

Page 81

1. c

2. b

3.

4.

5.

Representing Views of Three-Dimensional Shapes

Label the drawing that corresponds to the front view of each figure.

1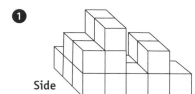

    a.   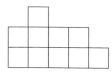   b.   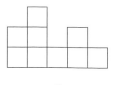   c.

    d.   e.

2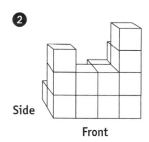

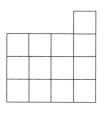   a.   b.   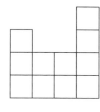   c.

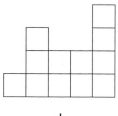   d.   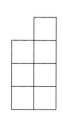   e.

Draw the front and side views of each figure.

3 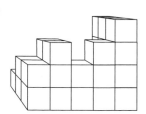   **4** 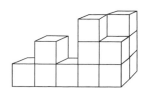   **5**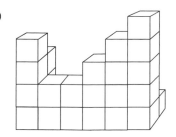

Representing Views of Three-Dimensional Shapes

Identify the correct base-layer or top-view drawing for each figure.

1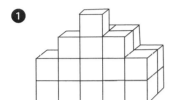

		4	3	3
2	3	4	3	2

a.

2		3	3	3
2	3	4	3	2

b.

		3	3	2
2	3	4	3	2

c.

2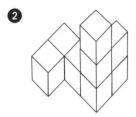

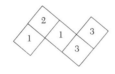

a.

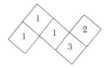

b.

c.

Create a base-layer or top-view drawing with numbers for each figure.

3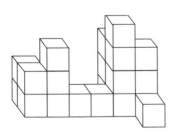

4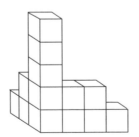

5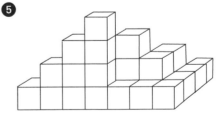

Analyzing Transformations and Congruence

Introduction

Objective → Students will describe transformations that could be used to move a geometric figure onto a congruent figure.

Context → Students have worked with congruent geometric figures. They will go on to study transformations that produce similar figures and use properties of figures to solve problems and create informal proofs.

NCTM Standards Focus

In this lesson students will use slides, reflections, or rotations to demonstrate that one figure can be moved onto another to show that the two are congruent. As students explore these transformations, they will observe patterns in the coordinates of the vertices of the congruent figures. They will use these patterns to write rules for making transformations of any polygon.

Representation Students use drawings to represent congruent figures on a coordinate plane. They then represent the transformations algebraically.

Reasoning and Proof Students identify patterns in the coordinates of vertices of congruent polygons. They write rules to describe each type of transformation, testing the validity of their rules with examples.

Communication Communication is an important focus of the lesson since there are many observations and ideas for students to share. By discussing the different ways they have learned to characterize congruence, students recognize the complementary relationship of the approaches.

Teaching Plan

Materials → Student pages 86–87; index cards; scissors; straightedge; grid paper

BEGIN THE LESSON by reviewing the meaning of congruence. Show students a drawing of two congruent figures and have them explain how they know whether the figures are congruent. Students should explain that congruent figures have the same size and shape, and that the measures of corresponding angles and sides are equal. You may wish to have students provide some real-world examples of congruence, such as each of the stamps in a roll, two pennies in their pockets, or a mirror image of themselves.

Distribute an index card to each student and instruct students to draw a diagonal across the rectangular card. *Is the diagonal a line of symmetry for the rectangle?* (No.) *Are the two triangles formed by the diagonal congruent?* (Yes.) Challenge students to prove congruence without measuring or physically moving the triangles. Encourage students to share all their solution ideas.

What Students Might Say

- The diagonal forms one side of each triangle.
- The opposite sides of the rectangle have the same length.
- The angles opposite the diagonals are both right angles.
- The other angles match up because they are formed by the diagonal.

Would cutting the rectangle on the diagonal and matching the triangles prove congruence. Why? (Yes. If two figures are congruent, they will fit exactly on one another.) Have students cut and match the triangles. Tell them to make notes of the moves they use. Urge them to reform the rectangle and repeat the moves, if necessary, to keep track, or to try different sequences of moves to find the fewest. As students describe the moves, be sure they are using the terms *slide* (*translation*), *flip* (*reflection*), and *turn* (*rotation*) correctly. You might also suggest students position the two triangles on their desks in various ways and describe how one triangle can be moved to fit on or coincide with the other.

D ISTRIBUTE STUDENT PAGE 86 and ask students to look at the first coordinate grid showing triangles 1 and 2. Have students work in pairs to decide what transformation(s) could be used to move triangle 1 onto triangle 2, thus showing congruence. Tell students to identify the coordinates of corresponding vertices of each triangle and record them on page 86. Suggest they examine the coordinates and look for a relationship.

Ask students to supply the two sets of coordinates and record them on the board. Then ask questions to help students note relationships between the vertices of the figures on the grid and their coordinates.

- *What transformation occurred here?* (A slide; triangle 1 slid 6 units to the left.)
- *Which coordinates changed? How?* (The *x*-coordinate for each vertex changed by -6; the *y*-coordinates stayed the same.)
- *Suppose you wanted to shift triangle 1 to the right 5 units to form another congruent triangle,* $\triangle$*GHI. Predict how you think the coordinates would change and record your predictions in the spaces on page 86.* (Students should predict that for a move 5 spaces right, each *x*-coordinate would change by $+5$, while the *y*-coordinates would remain unchanged.)

Instruct students to draw the triangle with the vertices they predicted and then check to see if their prediction was correct.

Now ask students to work together to write a set of general rules that tell how the coordinates of a figure change when the figure is moved *a* units to the left or right. (The rule to move *a* units to the left is $(x - a, y)$; the rule to move *a* units to the right is $(x + a, y)$.

DIRECT STUDENTS' ATTENTION TO the second set of figures on page 86.

- *How can triangle 4 be shifted onto triangle 5? Write the coordinates for corresponding vertices and explain how the coordinates changed.* (The *y*-coordinate of each vertex changed by $+5$; the *x*-coordinates stayed the same.)

- *Predict the coordinates for a congruent triangle, $\triangle STU$, created by moving triangle 4 down 2.* (The *y*-coordinates change by -2; the *x*-coordinates are unchanged.)

Have students draw the triangle and check their predictions.

- *How was each point of the original figure moved?* (Each point slid the same distance and in the same direction.)

- *What rule tells how the coordinates of a figure change when the figure is moved* b *units up or down?* [up $(x, y + b)$; down $(x, y - b)$]

DISTRIBUTE STUDENT PAGE 87 and have students examine the congruent triangles shown. Ask students to describe the transformation needed to move triangle 7 onto triangle 8, record the coordinates of corresponding vertices, and identify the pattern. (The triangle was reflected through the *x*-axis; the *x*-coordinates do not change; the *y*-coordinates have been multiplied by $^-1$.) Then ask students to predict the coordinates if the triangle was reflected through the *y*-axis, graph the triangle, and have them verify their predictions. $(^-x, y)$ Ask students to summarize the rules for reflections.

If time allows, have students work together to draw two congruent polygons on a coordinate plane such that two or more transformations would be needed to move one figure onto the other. Have students trade papers and describe the movements and coordinates for the transformations.

Extension

Have students explore the pattern of coordinates when a polygon is rotated 90° clockwise about the origin $[(x, y) \rightarrow (y, {}^-x)]$ and 180° clockwise about the origin $[(x, y) \rightarrow ({}^-x, {}^-y)]$. Students can also write pairs of transformations that are equivalent to the 180° rotation—two reflections.

Student Pages

Student page 86 and the top of student page 87 include the pairs of congruent triangles and recording space related to the lesson activities. The bottom of student page 87 provides exercises involving figures that are shifted using one or two transformations.

Assessment

It was possible to assess students' understanding of basic definitions of congruence during the introductory activity. As students described transformations, identified patterns in coordinates, made predictions, and drew congruent figures, there were many opportunities to judge their understanding of the geometric principles and their proficiency in working with coordinates. The rules students developed provided a measure of their overall understanding of transformations.

NCTM Standards Summary

This lesson involved the students in exploring and describing geometric transformations in a way that builds a foundation for future studies in analytic geometry. By identifying patterns and generalizing those patterns as rules, students translated their visual understanding into abstract symbolic representation. Students reasoned to extend the ideas of each activity through a process of prediction and verification. Because of the multiple concepts involved in this lesson, the emphasis on communication helped all students to gain insight into the key relationships.

Answers

Page 86
1. Triangle 1: $A = (6, 1)$, $B = (1, 1)$, $C = (2, 3)$;
   Triangle 2: $D = (0, 1)$, $E = ({}^-5, 1)$, $F = ({}^-4, 3)$
2. Slide to the left 6 units
3. $G = (11, 1)$, $H = (6, 1)$, $I = (7, 3)$
4. Slide left $(x - a, y)$; slide right $(x + a, y)$
5. Triangle 4: $M = (5, {}^-9)$, $N = (2, {}^-9)$, $O = (4, {}^-6)$;
   Triangle 5: $P = (5, {}^-4)$, $Q = (2, {}^-4)$, $R = (4, {}^-1)$
6. Slide up 5 units
7. $S = (5, {}^-11)$, $T = (2, {}^-11)$, $U = (4, {}^-8)$
8. Up $(x, y + a)$; down $(x, y - a)$

Page 87
1. Triangle 7: $J = (2, 1)$, $K = (6, 5)$, $L = (6, 1)$;
   Triangle 8: $W = (2, {}^-1)$, $X = (6, {}^-5)$, $Y = (6, {}^-1)$
2. Reflection over the x-axis
3. $({}^-2, 1)$, $({}^-6, 5)$, $({}^-6, 1)$
4. Over the x-axis $(x, {}^-y)$; over the y-axis $({}^-x, y)$
5. *A:* Slide down 8 units
   B: Reflection over the y-axis
   C: Slide up 2 units; slide to the left 7 units
   D: Slide down 5 units; slide to the left 10 units

Analyzing Transformations and Congruence

Use the figures to answer the questions.

❶ Write the coordinates for each triangle above.

❷ Describe the transformation that occurred from triangle 1 to 2.

❸ Predict the coordinates for triangle 1 if shifted 5 units right. Verify your prediction by graphing the triangle.

❹ Write a general rule for horizontal slides.

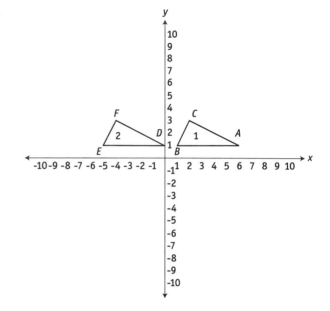

❺ Write the coordinates for each triangle at the right.

❻ Describe the transformation that occurred from triangle 4 to 5.

❼ Predict the coordinates for triangle 4 if shifted down 2 units. Verify your prediction by graphing the triangle.

❽ Write a general rule for vertical slides.

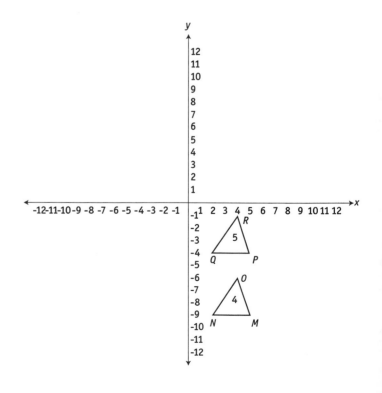

Standard 3 Geometry

Analyzing Transformations and Congruence

Use the figures to answer the questions.

1 Write the coordinates for each triangle.

2 Describe the transformation that occurred from triangle 7 to 8.

3 Predict the coordinates for triangle 7 if reflected over the *y*-axis. Verify your prediction by graphing the triangle.

4 Write a general rule for a reflection over the *x*-axis and for a reflection over the *y*-axis.

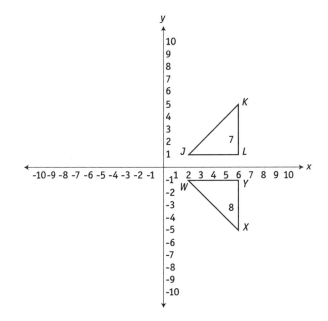

5 Describe the transformation of Figure *M* that is needed to make it coincide with each congruent figure.

Figure *A*

Figure *B*

Figure *C*

Figure *D*

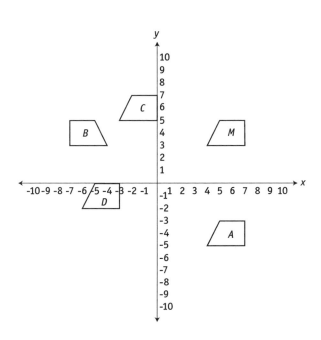

Investigating Angle-Sum Relationships

Introduction

Objective → Students will find the sum of the measures of the angles of triangles and quadrilaterals.

Context → This lesson is in the middle of a geometry unit in which students have learned about angles and relationships of pairs of angles and have classified triangles and quadrilaterals. They will go on to study angles related to parallel and perpendicular lines and work on constructions.

Investigating Angle-Sum Relationships

Learn

Activity A. Work in groups.

Draw and label and cut out the triangle. Mark the midpoints of $\overline{XY}$ and $\overline{XZ}$.

Now, fold the triangle so that vertex X touches $\overline{YZ}$.

Fold Y and Z over as shown to touch the vertex X.

$$m\angle Y + m\angle X + m\angle Z = 180°$$

Activity B.

Tear off the vertices of a paper quadrilateral $ABCD$. Arrange them around one vertex.

$$m\angle A + m\angle B + m\angle C + m\angle D = 360°$$

The sum of the measures of the angles of any quadrilateral is 360°.

Try

Find the measure of $\angle A$ in each figure.

1.

2.

3.

Practice

Tell whether each figure is possible.

1. A triangle with angles that measure 36°, 70°, and 70°.

2. A right triangle with angles that measure 40°, and 26°.

NCTM Process Standards Analysis and Focus

The standards analysis examines how the process standards have been incorporated into the above lesson. By increasing the focus on three of the process standards, a more effective and meaningful lesson can be presented. The suggestions offered can help you to think about how this might be accomplished.

Connections The lesson is based on the fact that a straight angle has a measure of 180°, but this connection is not clearly made. Similarly, the connection between the total degrees in a quadrilateral and the number of degrees in a circle is implied but not explicitly made.

Suggestion → **Enable students to make and verify the connection between a straight angle and the sum of the angle**

More Practice

Tell whether each figure is possible.

1. A triangle with angles that measure 40°, 26°, and 90°.

2. A quadrilateral with angles that measure 30°, 40°, 150°, and 140°.

3. A quadrilateral with angles that measure 80°, 90°, 100° and 110°.

4. A quadrilateral with 3 right angles and an angle that measures 100°.

5. A quadrilateral with angles that measure 70°, 75°, 120°, and 115°.

Apply

6. A triangle has two of its angles measuring 24° and 76°. What is the measure of the third angle?

7. A quadrilateral has angles of 76°, 110°, and 88°. What is the measure of the fourth angle?

8. An angle of a triangle measures 48°. The other two angles have equal measures. What is the measure of the angles?

9. A triangle has two angles measuring 37° and 36°. Estimate the measure of the third triangle. Is the triangle obtuse or acute?

Problem Solving

10. You have a triangle with angles of 35°, 110° and 35°. What figures can you make and place next to the triangle to make a rectangle? Solution: You can make two triangles with angles 55°, 35° and 90°, and place them next to the triangle forming a rectangle.

    a. Now try to make a rectangle starting with a triangle that has angles of 60°, 50° and 70°.

Critical Thinking

11. How many obtuse angles can a quadrilateral have? Explain your answer.

12. Can a triangle have a right and an obtuse angle? Explain.

measures of a triangle. Making this connection will give students a base from which other angle relationships can be developed. Have students divide quadrilaterals into triangles to determine the sum of the measures of the angles of a quadrilateral. Since this method generalizes to other polygons, familiarizing students with this procedure reinforces how mathematical ideas build on one another to create a larger, unified body of knowledge.

Reasoning and Proof Questions in the lesson involve simple arithmetic rather than reasoning. A few exercises ask students to explain the thinking used to derive their answers.

Suggestion → Encourage students to apply reasoning to determine angle relationships in triangles and quadrilaterals. Doing so and then explaining their thinking will help

students become better problem solvers and make them less reliant on rote learning.

Representation The lesson uses geometric drawings to represent figures.

Suggestion → Provide an opportunity for students to explore relationships through paper folding. Show students how to represent quadrilaterals as two triangles to enable them to understand why the sum of the angles in quadrilaterals total 360°. This representation will lay the foundation for a method that can be extended to find the total degrees in the angles of other polygons.

Problem Solving The lesson presents an exploration activity but then provides most of the answers to be found. Only one method is presented to find the sum of the angles in a quadrilateral.

Communication The lesson does not take advantage of opportunities that exist for students to discuss their thinking.

f.y.i.

The folding method for verifying
that the three angles of a triangle form a straight line is an
interesting activity. It is strongly
recommended that you try this
exercise yourself with different
types of triangles before presenting the lesson.

The teaching plan that follows shows how the suggestions for increasing the
focus on the process standards can be implemented.

Revised Teaching Plan

BEGIN THE LESSON BY DESCRIBING a situation for students to
consider. *Suppose you measured the angles of a triangle and found the
sum. You did this many times and each time the sum was 180° (or very close
to it because of measurement inaccuracies). What might you conclude?*
(The sum of the angle measures is 180° for any triangle.) *Now suppose you
wanted to verify your thinking. If you could show that the angles of a triangle formed a straight line, how would that prove you were correct?* (The
measure of a straight line is 180°. If the angles form a straight line, they
must total 180°.) This discussion motivates students' interest in the triangle
activities and makes the connection between geometric relationships.

Describe two methods students can use to verify these angle relationships—
one by folding a triangle as shown on the reduced text pages at the beginning of the lesson, and the second by cutting off the angles of a triangle
and combining them.

HAVE PAIRS OF STUDENTS work together on the activities. Encourage
students to work with triangles of different shapes and to be sure to represent extremes to see if the shape of the triangle matters. For example, have
them check triangles with one or two very small angles, triangles with angles
that are fairly equal, and triangles in which the lengths of the sides vary
greatly. Discuss why it is important to test a variety of triangles. Students
should be able to reason that if the angles of a triangle are said to form a
straight line, then that outcome should be true for all triangles, not just for
a few that happen to support the statement. Figuring out how to fold some
of the triangles may prove to be an interesting challenge for your students.

By observing pairs as they work, you can assess students' understanding of
the activity and their facility with the methods. You might also suggest that
students measure angles with a protractor and find the sum as another
method of checking.

What Might Happen . . . What to Do

Students may try the folding method with right triangles and experience a great deal of frustration in getting the angles to come together. The approach for dealing with this special set of triangles shown here should be demonstrated regardless of whether a problem arises, and students should test several different right triangles to verify the method.

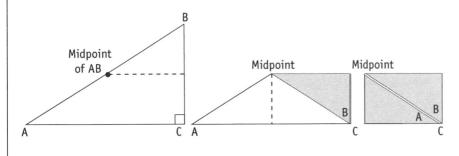

Demonstrate the method shown for folding a right triangle, and have students test several different right triangles to verify this method. *Why does this method of folding only validate the 180° measure for the angles of right triangles?* (If one angle is known to be a right angle, and the other two together form a right angle, the three add up to 180°.)

GUIDE STUDENTS TO DISCOVER other angle relationships by applying the basic result for a triangle. *We know the sum of the measures of the angles of any triangle is 180°. If you know the measures of two angles of a triangle, could you find the measure of the third angle? How would you do this?* While this is not a difficult question, answering it requires students to reason through the information they know and formulate a procedure. Provide a few examples for students to test their thinking. *Could the angles of a triangle measure 68°, 76°, and 55°?* (No.) *Explain.* (The sum would be 199°, and the sum of the angles for a triangle must be 180°.)

CONTINUE TO CONNECT to prior knowledge about angles and triangles. *What is the sum of the measures of the other two angles of a right triangle? Explain.* (A right angle measures 90°; since 180° − 90° = 90°, the sum of the other two angle measures must be 90°.) *What name is given to a pair of angles whose measures add to 90°?* (Complementary) This discussion provides the opportunity for students to reason with what they already know to develop another angle relationship.

NEXT, PROMPT STUDENTS to think about ways to find the sum of the measures of a quadrilateral. Actively seeking solutions encourages students to become problem solvers. *What do you know about the angles of rectangles and squares that might help determine the number of degrees in the four angles of those figures?* (Both figures have four right angles, a right angle is 90°, and 4 × 90° = 360°.) *Do you think all quadrilaterals have 360°? How about a trapezoid or parallelogram? How could we check?* Some students might suggest combining angles to form a circle; others might suggest measuring with a protractor. Accept suggestions and offer a third approach. Show students how to divide a rectangle into two triangles by drawing a diagonal from one vertex to another inside the figure. Representing a quadrilateral as two triangles and combining their 180° measures results in a total of 360° for the figure. This approach builds on established knowledge and lays a foundation for future explorations of finding total angle measure with other polygons.

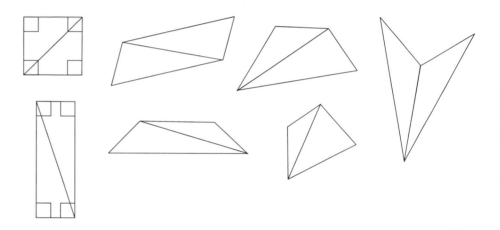

Clarify the use of the diagonals by having students divide a variety of quadrilateral figures into triangles. *Does it matter which diagonal we draw?* (No, two triangles are formed from either diagonal.) *How can dividing this figure into two triangles help us find the sum of degrees contained in its four angles?* (There are 180° in each of the two triangles, so there are 360° all together.) *Would the result be the same for any quadrilateral?* (Yes, any quadrilateral can be divided this way.) *How do you know?* (The drawings show this.) *Does using this method tell us the measure in a particular angle?* (No.) This discussion promotes logical thinking and highlights for students how mathematical knowledge continually builds on relationships that they already know.

CLOSE THE LESSON by presenting quadrilaterals with three angle measurements given and having students figure out the measure of the fourth angle.

Extension

Have students use the method of dividing a figure into triangles to find the sum of the measures of the angles of pentagons, hexagons, and so on. Students might also study the relationship between the number of sides a polygon has and the number of triangles it can be divided into to see if they can discover a pattern.

Student Pages

Students should be well prepared to complete exercises similar to those on the reduced student pages.

Assessment

As students worked on cutting and folding activities and answered questions in class, there were opportunities to assess their understanding of angle relationships and computational methods as well as their thinking skills.

NCTM Standards Summary

The lesson offered students opportunities to make connections to prior knowledge as they reasoned about new angle relationships. By relating total degrees in straight angles and triangles and then relating triangles to quadrilaterals, students were able to build on their own learning. Understanding the key outcome about the sum of the measures of the angles of a triangle allowed students to develop the steps for finding a missing measure, thus making the procedure more meaningful. Through reasoning, students identified the complementary angle relationship in right triangles. The representation of quadrilaterals as a combination of triangles provided the necessary connection for students to identify the angle sum for quadrilaterals. Moreover, this representation prepared students for later work with other polygons.

Standard 4 **Measurement**

AT THE SEVENTH GRADE LEVEL, measurement includes work with ratios and rates, finding the perimeter and area of two-dimensional figures, and finding the volume and surface area of rectangular and other geometric solids. Our lessons are derived from these important topics, and include a lesson on unit rates, a lesson that relates perimeter and area, a lesson that explores how surface area can change while the volume remains constant, and a lesson on finding the volume of pyramids and cones.

Three lessons model how the process standards can be used to teach content. A fourth lesson is a hypothetical textbook lesson that we have revised to be more standards based. These four lessons do not represent the entire curriculum, but rather provide glimpses of how, with a more concentrated effort to incorporate the process standards, better mathematics teaching and learning can be achieved.

In one lesson we have chosen, students make comparisons using unit rates. Through the process standards of reasoning and proof, connections, and communication, students see how unit rates are important in their everyday experiences as good consumers. Students solve problems by making decisions based on their knowledge of unit rates and support their answers.

Another lesson we have chosen relates perimeter and area. Students solve maximum and minimum problems while keeping one of the measures constant. This lesson incorporates the process standards of problem solving, reasoning and proof, and representation to solve real-world problems by making pictures and tables. Students make predictions and verify them.

A third lesson we have chosen is one that relates surface area and volume. Through the process standards of representation, reasoning and proof, and connections, there are two main points established in this lesson. Students explore how the surface area changes as the volume is held constant and try to generalize about the figures that yield the greatest and least surface areas, and what effect multiplying the dimensions of a figure by a constant factor has on surface area and volume.

The hypothetical textbook lesson we have chosen to revise is one in which students find the volume of a pyramid and of a cone. Through better incorporation of the process standards of connections, representation, and reasoning and proof, students derive the formulas for the volume from the formulas for the volume of a rectangular prism and a cylinder, rather than having them presented as a separate concept. Students also show how, if the manipulatives are available, the relationships between pyramids and prisms, and cones and cylinders.

Standard 4 Lessons

Investigating Unit Rates

Relating Area and Perimeter

Exploring Surface Area
and Volume

Investigating Volume
of Pyramids and Cones

Investigating Unit Rates

Introduction

- -

Objective → Students will make comparisons using unit rates.

Context → This lesson comes toward the end of a unit on ratio and proportion. Students have learned how to use proportions to solve basic rate problems. They will continue to apply ratio concepts as they work with scale drawings and analyze similar polygons.

NCTM Standards Focus

By making real-life comparisons and representing situations that involve unit rate comparisons, students will recognize the usefulness of unit rates in daily life. They will develop an understanding of unit rates by considering a problem that they might encounter and then explore more complex situations that involve converting units before a meaningful comparison can be made. Students will recognize the need to examine each problem situation carefully in order to use the numerical information correctly.

Reasoning and Proof Students explain the methods they use to make comparisons. They identify how problems differ and suggest the steps needed to accommodate these differences. Students will make decisions based on given data and support their choices.

Connections Students use unit rates to describe real-life situations and make comparisons that involve everyday activities such as shopping or working. As they solve problems, students rely on prior knowledge about metric and customary units.

Communication Students present solutions and share their methods, both orally and in writing. They discuss factors other than unit rate that may influence consumer decisions.

Teaching Plan

Materials → Student pages 100–101

MOTIVATE THE DISCUSSION of unit rates by presenting the following situation for students to consider.

> Two competing video stores offer Frequent Renter Programs. At MegaVideo, you get 2 free rentals for every 15 paid rentals; at Videorama, you get 3 free rentals for every 20 paid rentals.

Establish that the problem is more complicated than deciding that 3 free videos are better than 2 free videos. Ask students to determine which store offers a better deal and to explain how they made their decision. Have students share their responses and methods.

Methods Students Might Use

- Some students will use division to arrive at the conclusion that MegaVideo is offering 1 free rental for every 7.5 videos that are paid for, while Videorama is offering 1 free rental for every 6.67 paid for, so Videorama has the better offer.

- Some students may find a common multiple of 15 and 20 and determine that MegaVideo gives 8 free rentals for every 60 that are paid for, while Videorama gives 9 free rentals for every 60 that are paid for.

Have students compare the two methods. They should note that in the first method, the cost for one video was found, while in the second method, the number of free videos received for an equal number of paid for videos were compared. Explain that the first method is an example of finding a unit rate. Students will accept the formal concept of unit rates when they realize that they have already reasoned through how they are calculated.

REMIND STUDENTS THAT A RATE is a ratio that compares two different quantities. The simplest form of a rate has a denominator of 1 unit and is called a *unit rate*. Driving 250 miles in 5 hours would be an example of a ratio or rate; the unit rate would represent the distance driven in one hour, or 50 miles/1 hour.

Reinforce this concept by presenting another rate and asking students to determine the unit rate. *If Lisa types 135 words in 3 minutes, what is her unit rate?* Students should respond that Lisa's unit rate is 45 words per minute. Write the ratios on the board for emphasis.

$$\frac{135 \text{ words}}{3 \text{ minutes}} = \frac{45 \text{ words}}{1 \text{ minute}}$$

Explain that in stores, the unit price of an item is a price per unit of measure. *Why is unit pricing helpful for a consumer?* (Unit prices help you to compare the prices of two different sizes or brands of a product.) Emphasize that to compare two unit prices, both must be expressed using the same unit. This idea will be further explored after the students carry out basic calculations. Reinforce the proportion method that students have learned by writing another proportion on the board:

$$\frac{\text{unit price}}{\text{one unit}} = \frac{\text{price of package}}{\text{\# of units in package}}$$

POINT OUT THAT since the denominator of the first ratio is 1, this expression can simply be written as *unit price = price of package/number of units in package*. You may also wish to point out that the unit price of a product is usually rounded to the nearest $\frac{1}{10}$ of a cent. However, if someone actually buys only one item, stores always round up to the next cent. For example, the unit price of oranges at 3 for $1.00 is 33.3¢ per orange, but at the counter the customer would pay 34¢ for one orange.

Present the following problem for students to solve individually.

> **At the supermarket, a 5-pound pack of rice sells for $3.59, while a 20-pound sack sells for $12.99. Which is the better buy? Explain your method.**

Allow students a few minutes to work, then have them discuss their work. Students should explain that they wrote a ratio of the price to the number of units for each size, found unit ratios, then compared the unit prices. Since the 5-pound pack has a unit price of 71.8¢ and the 20-pound sack has a unit price of 65¢, the 20-pound size is the better buy.

Continue the discussion by asking students to consider factors, other than unit price, that might influence a shopper's choice. They may point out that a person might not have storage space for a less expensive larger size or, if the product is used infrequently, may end up throwing out ununsed merchandise. If the unit prices relate to different brands, such as a national brand versus a supermarket or generic brand, the quality or flavor of the product must be considered. For example, if more of a less expensive brand of detergent is needed to get clothes clean, it may not be a better buy.

NEXT, HELP STUDENTS EXAMINE unit prices when ratios are expressed in different units.

- *Which is the better buy, 0.375 kilograms of cheese for $4.98 or 100 grams for $1.20?*
- *How is this problem different than the problem about the rice?* (The quantities are expressed using different units.)
- *What must you do first to solve this problem?* (Convert the units for one of the quantities.)
- *Which quantity will you convert? Why?* (Students may explain that it is easier to work with whole numbers, so they will convert 0.375 kg to 375 grams.)

Have students complete the problem and share their findings. (The larger size of cheese (0.375 kg) costs 1.3¢ per gram while the smaller size costs only 1.2¢ per gram.)

CONCLUDE THE LESSON with a brief discussion of how it is often possible to determine unit rates using mental math.

> **Suppose Joyce read 280 words in 8 minutes. Can you find a way to mentally determine Joyce's reading rate? Explain your method.**

If using repeated division does not occur to students, suggest this approach by explaining that 280 words in 8 minutes is the same as 140 words in 4 minutes, 70 words in 2 minutes, and 35 words in 1 minute. Encourage all students use this method to find the unit price of one CD if 12 equally priced CD's cost $156. ($156 for 12; $78 for 6; $39 for 3; $13 for 1)

Student Pages

Student page 100 presents situations requiring students to find unit rates and prices. On student page 101, students solve problems involving comparisons and are provided with a space for recording and analyzing price data from their own research.

Assessment

As they worked through examples, it was possible to observe students' strategies for solving unit rate problems. As students answered questions and made calculations, you could assess their proficiency at finding rates and determining best buys. Individual evaluation of understanding could be determined from responses to the exercises and the project on the student pages.

NCTM Standards Summary

In this lesson, students used their own reasoning processes to develop the fundamental idea of unit rates. They applied the lesson concepts to real-life situations and made connections to other measurement skills. They reasoned as they accommodated more complex comparison situations to create units that were the same to compare rates. As they discussed various factors that influence purchase decisions and explained their thinking, students communicated their understanding of unit rates.

Answers

Page 100

1. a
2. b
3. a
4. a
5. b
6. b
7. a
8. b
9. Ready to serve
10. Stan

Project—Answers will vary.

Page 101

1. $\frac{228 \text{ miles}}{6 \text{ hours}}$; 38 miles per hour

2. $\frac{372 \text{ students}}{12 \text{ teachers}}$; 31 students per teacher

3. $\frac{\$47.95}{7 \text{ hours}}$; $6.85 per hour

4. $\frac{\$5.40}{12 \text{ bagels}}$; $0.45 per bagel

5. $\frac{57 \text{ sit-ups}}{3 \text{ minutes}}$; 19 sit-ups per minute

6. $\frac{500 \text{ words}}{8 \text{ minutes}}$; 62.5 words per minute

7. $\frac{216 \text{ miles}}{16 \text{ gal}}$; 13.5 miles per gal

8. $\frac{36 \text{ commercials}}{2 \text{ hours}}$; 18 commercials per hour

9. $\frac{4.4¢}{\text{oz}}$

10. $\frac{\$5.69}{\text{lb}}$

11. $\frac{3.1¢}{\text{oz}}$

12. $\frac{31.7¢}{\text{can}}$

13. $\frac{\$2.839}{\text{kg}}$

14. $\frac{24.5¢}{\text{oz}}$

15. $\frac{99.5¢}{\text{L}}$

16. $\frac{74¢}{\text{pair}}$

17. $\frac{33.3¢}{\text{bar}}$

18. $\frac{\$14.148}{\text{kg}}$

Investigating Unit Rates

Determine the better buy. Ring a or b.

1. applesauce   a. 24 oz. for $1.25   b. 16 oz. for $0.89
2. grape juice   a. $\frac{1}{2}$ gal for $2.80 b. 20 oz. for $0.75
3. olive oil   a. 3L for $16.99   b. 500 mL for $3.09
4. cat litter   a. 5 lb for $3.78   b. 20 lb for $15.50
5. ground beef   a. 4.3 kg for $21.70   b. 1.6 kg for $7.85
6. hamburger rolls   a. 3 bags of 8 for $2.98   b. 4 bags of 10 for $4.25
7. ribbon   a. 5 m for $6.45   b. 240 cm for $3.19
8. greeting cards   a. 3 boxes of 12 for $30.00   b. 4 boxes of 15 for $49.00

9. An 11-ounce can of condensed soup, to which you must add 1 can of water, costs $1.45. A 20-ounce can of ready-to-serve soup costs $1.29. Which is the better buy?

10. Stan typed 90 pages in 7.5 hours. Jan typed 110 pages in 9.4 hours. Who has the higher rate?

Project

Use supermarket fliers, newspaper ads, or visit the store to find prices for different brands of an item or same brand items that are available in different sizes. Name the item and list the information for each size or brand. Then determine the better buy.

Item	Package Size/Price	Package Size/Price

Investigating Unit Rates

Express each ratio as a unit rate. An example is shown.

Ratio	Rate	Unit Rate
❶ 228 miles in 6 hours	$\dfrac{228\ miles}{6\ hours}$	38 miles per hour
❷ 372 students for 12 teachers		
❸ $47.95 for 7 hours		
❹ $5.40 for 1 dozen bagels		
❺ 57 sit-ups in 3 minutes		
❻ 500 words read in 8 minutes		
❼ 216 miles on 16 gallons of gas		
❽ 36 commercials in 2 hours of TV		

Find the unit price of each item. Round to the nearest tenth of a cent.

❾ 64 oz of orange juice for $2.79

❿ 5 pounds of roast beef for $28.45

⓫ 16 oz of spaghetti for $0.50

⓬ 24 cans of dog food for $7.60

⓭ 7 kg of chicken for $19.87

⓮ 6.5 oz tuna for $1.59

⓯ 2.2 L cola for $2.19

⓰ 12 pairs of socks for $8.88

⓱ 1.5 dozen granola bars for $5.99

⓲ 4.4 kg of cashews for $62.25

Relating Area and Perimeter

Introduction

Objective → Students will solve maximum/minimum problems involving fixed perimeters or areas.

Context → Students know how to determine both the perimeter/circumference and area of rectangles, triangles, and circles. After investigating the variation in area or perimeter when one of the measures is fixed, they will go on to investigate similar relationships for surface area and volume.

NCTM Standards Focus

Students will use an organized approach to explore the possible areas for a fixed perimeter and the possible perimeters for a fixed area. By observing patterns of variation, students will be able to make generalizations about figures that maximize or minimize one measure while the other measure remains constant.

Problem Solving Students explore area and perimeter and solve maximum/minimum problems in real-world situations. They interpret practical constraints such as *least cost for fencing* or *greatest garden space* in mathematical terms.

Reasoning and Proof Students generalize patterns of change in area or perimeter. They make predictions based on their ideas and verify them. Students identify and describe the common property of regularity that yields maximum area within a class of polygons.

Representation Students represent figures with drawings and organize tables of areas and perimeters. They make drawings to represent the information in word problems, and they construct graphs to represent area and perimeter relationships.

Teaching Plan

Materials → Student pages 106–107

INTRODUCE THE LESSON by presenting a problem for students to consider. *Judy wants to fence off a rectangular garden in her backyard to grow tomatoes. She has 24 feet of fencing. What is the greatest or maximum area she can fence off? What are the dimensions of the rectangle?*

Begin discussion by asking students what the 24 feet of fencing represents. (The perimeter of the rectangle she can make.) Tell students to assume Judy wants to use only whole-number dimensions.

- *What are the dimensions of some rectangles Judy can make with her 24 feet of fencing? Make sketches to represent your solutions.* (Possible answers include 2 ft by 10 ft and 8 ft by 4 ft.)
- *How did you find the length and width?* Students may explain that $2l + 2w = 24$, or $2(l + w) = 24$, so $l + w = 12$. (By picking a number to represent one dimension, they can solve for the other.)

- *What is the area of each of these rectangular gardens? How do you know?* (Area = lw, so the area of a 2 ft by 10 ft garden is 20 sq. ft, and the area of the 8 ft by 4 ft garden is 32 sq. ft.)
- *Are there other rectangles with a perimeter of 24 feet?* (Yes.)
- *What is the largest dimension one rectangle can have?* (11 ft)

HAVE STUDENTS WORK individually or in pairs to make a table of rectangles with a perimeter of 24 feet and their corresponding areas. A table for recording information is found on student page 106. Write this table on the board while students work. When they are finished, ask students to provide the dimensions and areas they found and record the information on the board.

- *Which rectangle has the smallest or minimum area?* (1 ft by 11 ft; 11 sq. ft)
- *Which rectangle has the maximum area?* (6 ft by 6 ft; 36 sq. ft)
- *What is special about this rectangle?* (It is a square.)
- *Did you notice any pattern in your list of areas? How could this pattern shorten the work if you try similar problems?* (After 6 ft by 6 ft, the dimension pairs repeat so the areas repeat; the areas are symmetric about the maximum area for the square.)

Now present a similar problem with a different perimeter for students to consider. *Suppose Judy had 36 feet of fencing for a garden.*

- *Can you predict dimensions for the garden that would produce the maximum area? Explain.* (9 ft by 9 ft; A square produces the greatest area. Divide 36 ft by 4 to get 9 ft for each side.)
- *What would be the area of this garden?* (81 sq. ft)

Have students verify their answers by making another table of possible rectangles and corresponding areas. Then discuss whether their predictions were correct and if their tables showed patterns similar to those found in the first example.

Now ask students to consider what rectangle would give maximum area for 50 feet of fencing. Qualify the problem by stating that the dimensions must be whole numbers. *Can you make a square?* (No. The rectangle closest to a square is 12 ft by 13 ft, giving an area of 156 sq. ft.) *What if you could use any dimensions? How much more area could you get?* (A square with a

f.y.i.

Note that on student page 106 students will be asked to graph the area and perimeter relationships they find for rectangles with $P = 24$ feet.

perimeter of 50 ft would be 12.5 ft on a side. The area for this square would be 156.25 sq. ft; 0.25 sq. ft greater.)

NEXT, HAVE STUDENTS CONSIDER a different but related situation. *Leroy has decided he wants a garden with 64 square feet of space. Fencing costs $5 per foot, so he would like to use the least amount of fencing as possible to make his garden. What dimensions should he use? What will he spend for fencing?*

- *How is this problem different than the problems just solved?* (In the first set of problems, the perimeter was fixed and the area could vary. In this problem, the area is fixed and the perimeter can vary.)
- *How can you find all the rectangles with an area of 64 sq. ft, assuming the dimensions are whole numbers?* (Find the factors of 64.)
- *If a rectangle has a width of 1 ft, what length should it have to produce an area of 64 sq. ft?* (64 ft)
- *What would the perimeter of this rectangle be? Explain.* [$P = 2l + 2w$, so $P = 2(64) + 2(1) = 130$ ft]

Instruct students to make a table showing the perimeters of all rectangles with an area of 64 sq. ft. Point out that they can shorten the work by eliminating pairs of factors that repeat.

Length	Width	Area	Perimeter
64 ft	1 ft	64 sq. ft	130 ft
32 ft	2 ft	64 sq. ft	68 ft
16 ft	4 ft	64 sq. ft	40 ft
8 ft	8 ft	64 sq. ft	32 ft

- *Which rectangle has the smallest perimeter?* (An 8-ft square with a perimeter of 32 ft) *How much would it cost to fence this square?* ($160)
- *Suppose Leroy wanted a garden with an area of 100 sq. ft, how much would he have to spend on fencing? Explain.* ($200; a 10-ft square would have the minimum perimeter of 40 ft.)
- *What would be the least he could spend if he wanted a 72-sq. ft garden? Explain.* ($170; a 9 ft by 8 ft rectangle would have minimum perimeter of 34 ft.)

Answers

Page 106

1.

l(ft)	w (ft)	P (ft)	A (ft²)
1	11	24	11
2	10	24	20
3	9	24	27
4	8	24	32
5	7	24	35
6	6	24	36
7	5	24	35
8	4	24	23
9	3	24	27
10	2	24	20
11	1	24	11

(maximum area is 36 sq. ft)

2. Graph should show points that lie on a symmetric curve or arc; as length increases, area also increases, until length represents the side of a square. The areas are symmetric about the maximum area for the square.

3. $r \approx 3.8$ ft; $A \approx 45.3$ sq. ft

4. The area of circle (45.3 sq. ft) is greater than the maximum area of the rectangle (36 sq. ft).

5. The area of the circle (289.4 sq. ft) is greater than the maximum area of the rectangle (225 sq. ft.).

6. A circle has a greater area than the maximum area of a rectangle when both have the same perimeter/circumference.

CONCLUDE THE LESSON by posing questions that extend students' understanding by having them think about some general relationships for area and perimeter.

- *If the length and width of a rectangle are both doubled, how does the perimeter change?* (It is doubled.)
- *How does the area change?* (It is quadrupled.)
- *What will happen if length and width are tripled?* (Perimeter is tripled and area is multiplied by 9.)
- *What is the result if length and width are halved?* (Perimeter is halved and area is one-fourth.)
- *Explain a general rule.* (Students may suggest that if each dimension is multiplied by n, then the new perimeter is n times the original perimeter and the new area is n^2 times the original area.)

Student Pages

Student page 106 provides recording space for the lesson activity. Exercises are provided that allow students to continue their investigation of area and perimeter relationships through graphing and to consider fixed perimeters in relation to circles and triangles. Student page 107 has students use their understanding of the relationships between area and perimeter to solve more challenging problems.

Assessment

Throughout the lesson there were opportunities to assess whether students understood how to create different rectangles with a fixed perimeter or area and find maximum area or minimum perimeter. Student responses during discussions indicated their ability to generalize their results to other situations and express patterns of change in areas and perimeters.

NCTM Standards Summary

The lesson presented students with real-world situations that involved fixed measures and gave students the opportunity to solve problems by generating data and making an organized table of information. Reasoning was important as students examined data and generalized information about figures with minimum perimeter and maximum area. Representations, including drawings, tables, and graphs, provided visual help as students solved problems and discovered key relationships.

Page 107
1. $P = 24$ ft; $A = 24$ sq. ft
2. $P = 24$ ft; $A = 27.6$ sq. ft
3. $P = 24$ ft; $A = 19.6$ sq. ft
4. The triangle with 8 ft on each side has the greatest area. The greatest rectangular area is obtained when all sides have the same length.
5. Minimum perimeter is for a 12 in. by 15 in. rectangle with $P = 54$ in. Trim would cost $2.70.
6. 20 ft; 300 sq. ft

Relating Area and Perimeter

Complete the table.

1 Give the lengths and widths of all rectangles with a perimeter of 24 feet. Dimensions must be whole numbers. Then identify the maximum area.

length	width	perimeter	area

Maximum area _____

2 Graph the relation between pairs of lengths and areas shown in the table in Question 1. The point showing the relation for $l = 1$, $w = 11$ has already been placed on the graph. Describe your graph.

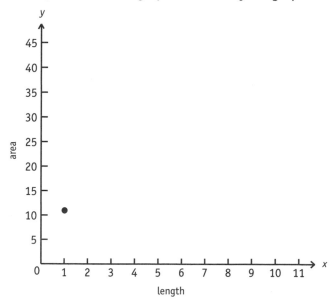

3 Find the radius for a circle with a circumference of 24 ft. Use $\pi \approx 3.14$ and round to the nearest tenth. Then find the area of that circle. (Use a calculator.)

4 Compare the area of the circle with $C = 24$ ft with the maximum rectangular area with $P = 24$ ft.

5 Compare the maximum area for a rectangle with $P = 60$ ft to the area of a circle with $C = 60$ ft.

6 What do the answers to Questions 4 and 5 suggest?

Standard 4 Measurement

Relating Area and Perimeter

Find the perimeter and area of each triangle. (Round to the nearest tenth.)

1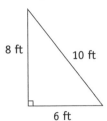

8 ft   10 ft

6 ft

2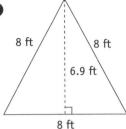

8 ft   8 ft

6.9 ft

8 ft

3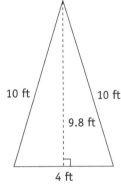

10 ft   10 ft

9.8 ft

4 ft

P = _____

A = _____

P = _____

A = _____

P = _____

A = _____

4 Which triangle had the greatest area? Explain how this result is similar to what you discovered for rectangles.

5 Rosita made a rectangular placemat with an area of 180 square inches. She used a braid trim around the edges. The braid cost 5¢ an inch. If Rosita spent the least amount possible to trim the mat, what were its dimensions? How much did the braid cost?

6 A rectangular lot is to be fenced, then divided down the middle by a fence to create two identical dog pens as shown. There is 120 feet of fencing available for the construction. What should the length and width of each pen be to maximize their area? What is the maximum area of each pen? Use any method to solve the problem.

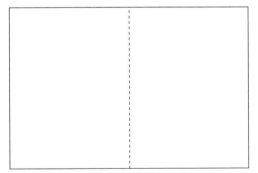

Exploring Surface Area and Volume

Introduction

Objective → Students will show how surface area varies for a fixed volume and explain how changes in linear dimensions affect surface area and volume.

Context → Students may have investigated relationships between perimeter and area and they have worked separately with the concepts of surface area and volume. They will go on to analyze composite figures, explore the relationship between mass and volume, and study geometric transformations.

NCTM Standards Focus

In this lesson, students will develop their understanding of the relationship between measures of surface area and volume. As they create concrete models, students will observe how surface area can vary as volume remains constant. They will continue to explore this concept more abstractly by listing the dimensions of all of the possible boxes with a given volume and then determining the surface area for each. Finally, they will probe deeper into the relationship by examining how changes in linear dimensions affect surface area and volume, and suggesting why the results occur.

Representation Students will create concrete models to study variation in surface area. They will make geometric drawings; represent dimensions of solid figures in organized tables; and represent relationships among linear, surface, and volume measures using ratios and variable expressions.

Reasoning and Proof Students will identify figures with greatest and least surface area for a fixed volume and will look for patterns. They will examine the effects of multiplying linear dimensions on both surface area and volume, and will formulate generalizations.

Connections In connecting surface area to problems involving cost of materials or advertising space, students rely on prior knowledge of factors, ratio, and exponents to compare surface areas and volumes. They will also recognize the connections among one-, two-, and three-dimensional measures.

Teaching Plan

Materials → Student pages 112–113; 8 unit cubes per student

BEGIN THE LESSON by distributing 8 loose unit cubes to each student and engaging the class in a brief review of volume and surface area. Ask students to identify the volume of a single cube and the total volume of all of eight cubes. (1 unit^3; 8 units^3) Ask them for the surface area of a single cube; then have them find the surface area for all eight of the cubes and explain how they found it. (6 units^2; 48 units^2; $8 \times 6 = 48$)

Now direct students to arrange the cubes in a 2×4 shape. Have students compare the models they create, and as you discuss the figures, verify that answers apply in all cases. *Is the volume still 8 cubic units? Explain.* (Yes; The volume or space inside each cube has not changed.) *Is the surface area still 48 square units?* (No.) *Why not?* (Some of the surfaces have been covered up.) *What is the surface area now?* (28 units²)

Next, instruct students to use all 8 cubes to build a cube. *What is the total volume of the cube you created?* (8 units³) *What is the total surface area of that cube? Explain.* (24 units²; each face has 4 square units and $6 \times 4 = 24$.)

DISTRIBUTE STUDENT PAGE 112. Divide students into work groups of 3 or 4, but instruct students that each one should create models individually. Ask students to build different shapes using all 8 cubes, draw a sketch, and determine the surface area for each shape. Stipulate that all cubes must share at least one complete face with another cube. Suggest students try both box shapes and irregular arrangements, and that they continue to work until they think they have found the greatest and least possible surface areas.

When students have completed the activity, discuss their results. They should have found even values ranging from 24–34 units² as possible surface areas. *What shape gave the greatest surface area?* (A $1 \times n$ row, which gave 34 units²) *Do you think that arrangement would always produce the greatest surface area? Explain.* (Yes; the fewest number of faces are covered up.) *What did you notice about the shape with the least surface area?* (It was a $2 \times 2 \times 2$ cube.) *Do you think that arrangement would produce the least surface area for other numbers of cubes?* Encourage students to explore this with their cubes. They should find the answer is yes. *How would you arrange 27 cubes to get the least surface?* ($3 \times 3 \times 3$ cube)

Now that students have seen for themselves that surface area can vary for a fixed volume, have them move on to another example.

> Swell Jells needs a cardboard box with a volume of 24 cubic inches for their jellybeans.

Have students determine dimensions for different boxes that Swell Jells can use. They should be able to name sets of three factors of 24 to consider for this purpose. Direct students to list the dimensions of all possible boxes in the space provided in Activity 2 on student page 112. Instruct them to verify that the volume is 24 cubic inches, and to find the surface area for each. Suggest that making a sketch of each box will help them do the calculations. Stipulate that dimensions must be whole numbers. Encourage students to share the work to save time.

f.y.i.

In the 2×4 shape there are 10 places where 2 faces are put together. Since there are 48 faces altogether, those 10 faces being put together cover up 20 faces. $48 - 20 = 28$. Pointing this out to students, and even having them check this with cubes, will help them to reason through other problems.

f.y.i.

An arrangement of cubes in a $1 \times n$ row will always result in the maximum surface area since this arrangement has the least number of faces covering each other. Sometimes other arrangements will produce an equivalent value. A cube will always result in the minimum surface area since that arrangement will have the greatest number of faces covering each other.

ENGAGE STUDENTS IN A DISCUSSION about their results. Have them give the dimensions for all of the possible boxes and their suface areas. (See Answers section for Activity 2.) Have them identify the set of dimensions that resulted in the greatest surface area (1 × 1 × 24 which gave *S.A.* of 98 in.²) and the least surface area (2 × 3 × 4 which, in this case, is closest to a cube and gave *S.A.* of 52 in.²). *Why might Swell Jells want the box with the least surace area?* (To minimize the amount of cardboard, and therefore, the cost for each box.) *Why might Swell Jells want a box with greater surface area?* (Possible answers include the extra area might be useful for advertising copy or nutritional information; the size might be displayed or shipped more conveniently, it is considered more attractive or different than a competitor's; or the package might be thought to contain more because it appears larger.)

NOW, PRESENT A NEW situation for students to consider.

> Suppose Swell Jells chose the box with dimensions of 2 × 3 × 4 inches. Then they decided they also wanted to market a larger size.

If Swell Jells doubles the height from 4 to 8 inches, will the volume of the box also double? (Yes; 2 × 3 × 8 = 48) *Would the surface area also double?* (No.) Have students find the surface area to verify that doubling does not occur; the new surface area is 92 in.² and 92 ≠ 2(52).

The situation above provides a transition into another important aspect of the surface area/volume relationship—that is, what happens when the linear dimensions are changed by a given factor. Invite students to explore what happens when one dimension is increased. *If you double the length of each 1-inch edge of a cube, what will the dimensions of the new cube be?* (2 × 2 × 2 inches) *What is the new surface area?* (6 × 4 = 24 in.) *How does this compare to the original area?* (It is 4 times as much.) Have students double the length of a cube measuring 1-inch on each edge, find the volume of the new cube, and compare the new volume to the original. Students should find that it is 8 times as much. Point out that each edge was doubled, or multiplied by a factor of 2, and discuss how that relates to producing a volume that is 8 times as great.

Answers

Page 112

Activity 1: Many arrangements are possible.

1. Answers will vary.

2. Greatest surface area: 43 units²; least surface area: 24 units²

Activity 2: All other boxes are equivalent to the 6 listed here.

Length (in.)	Width (in.)	Height (in.)	Volume (in.³)	Surface Area (in.²)
1	1	24	24	98
1	2	12	24	76
1	3	8	24	70
1	4	6	24	68
2	2	6	24	56
2	3	4	24	52

Activity 3

Length of Edge (in.)	Surface Area (in.²)	Volume (in.³)
1	6	1
2	24	8
3	54	27

3. 4; 8

4. 9; 27

5. m^2; m^3

Before pursuing generalizations, lead students through a similar set of questions for tripling each edge of the original cube. Then help students express the relationship as a general rule. *Suppose you multiply each edge of the cube by a factor of m. By what factor will the surface area increase?* (m^2) *The volume?* (m^3) *How can you explain this relationship?* (Students may suggest area is a square measure; you multiply side $\times$ side; volume is a cubic measure; you multiply side $\times$ side $\times$ side.)

Encourage students to express the relationships discussed using variables. Begin with the side of the original cube as s. [Original cube: s, $6s^2$, s^3; edge doubled: $2s$, $6(4s^2)$ $8s^3$; edge tripled: $3s$, $6(9s^2)$, $27s^3$] Students will then be ready to complete Activity 3 on student page 112. They will have progressed from studying the surface area/volume relationship using concrete models to an abstract characterization using variables.

Student Pages

Student page 112 provides recording space for activities in the lesson. Student page 113 includes additional exercises to reinforce and extend understanding of the relationship between surface area and volume.

Assessment

Reviewing basic concepts provided an opportunity to assess readiness for the lesson. You could judge their ability to find and compare surface areas as students worked with concrete models and compared dimensions for different boxes with a given volume. As they presented findings, you could determine if they correctly identified greatest and least surface area.

NCTM Standards Summary

In contrast to more traditional approaches that treat surface area and volume as two separate measures determined with various formulas, this activity-based lesson raised awareness of the relationship between the two through explorations. Students took advantage of various representations, including models, drawings, tables, and variable expressions, to identify patterns and draw conclusions about growth and form in three-dimensions. Students relied on prior knowledge about factors, ratio, and exponents to analyze their own information. By connecting to real-world situations, they recognized the significance of exploring these relationships.

Answers

Page 113

1. No; The volume of an $8 \times 6 \times 4$ box is 192 in.^{3}; at least $8 \times 32 = 256$ in.^{3} are needed.
2. Possible boxes are $16 \times 4 \times 4$ or $8 \times 8 \times 4$
3. $V = 256$ in.^{3}; S.A. of $16 \times 4 \times 4 = 288$ in.^{2}; S.A. of $8 \times 8 \times 4 = 256$ in.^{2}
4. False
5. True
6. True
7. False
8. True
9. 3:5
10. 54 in.^{2}; 150 in.^{2}
11. 54:150 or 9:25
12. 27 in.^{3}; 125 cm^3
13. 27:125
14. The ratio of the surface areas is the square of the ratio of the edges; the ratio of the volumes is the cube of the ratio of the edges; edges 3:5; surface areas $9:25 = 3^2:5^2$; volumes $27:125 = 3^3:5^3$

Exploring Surface Area and Volume

Activity 1

Arrange 8 unit cubes to make different shapes. Each face must share at least one other face with another cube. Draw your solutions.

1 Identify the surface area for each shape you created.

2 Identify the greatest and least surface areas.

Activity 2

Complete the table. Find the dimensions of boxes that have a volume of 24 cubic inches. Then find the surface area for each box.

Length	Width	Height	Volume	Surface Area

Activity 3

Complete the table by filling in the information for each cube. Then use the information in the table to complete each statement.

Length of Edge	Surface Area	Volume
1 inch		
2 inches		
3 inches		

3 When the edge of a cube is multiplied by 2, the surface area is multiplied by _____ and the volume is multiplied by _____.

4 When the edge of a cube is multiplied by 3, the surface area is multiplied by _____ and the volume is multiplied by _____

5 When the edge of a cube is multiplied by m, the surface area is multiplied by _____ and the volume is multiplied by _____.

Standard 4 Measurement

Exploring Surface Area and Volume

Suppose you wanted to pack 8 boxes that were each 4 in. × 2 in. × 4 in. so they just fit into a larger box.

❶ Could you pack the 8 boxes in a large box that was 8 in. × 6 in. × 4 in.? Explain how you know.

❷ Describe two different large boxes that would hold the 8 smaller boxes. Use words or a drawing to explain how the smaller boxes would be arranged.

❸ What is the volume of each of the two larger boxes? The surface area?

The height of a box is doubled and the other dimensions remain unchanged. Write true or false for each of the following.

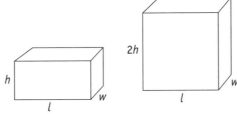

❹ The areas of the top and bottom are doubled.   **❺** The areas of the front and back are doubled.

❻ The areas of the left and right sides are doubled.   **❼** The total surface area is doubled.

❽ The volume is doubled.

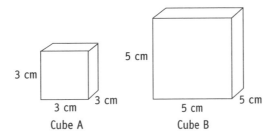

Refer to the picture of Cube A and Cube B.

❾ What is the ratio of the edge of Cube A to the edge of Cube B?

❿ What is the surface area of Cube A? of Cube B?

⓫ What is the ratio of the surface area of Cube A to the surface area of Cube B?

⓬ What is the volume of Cube A? of Cube B?

⓭ What is the ratio of the volume of Cube A to the volume of Cube B?

⓮ Examine your answers above. Explain any relationships you notice.

Investigating Volume of Pyramids and Cones

Introduction

Objective → Students will determine volumes of pyramids and cones.

Context → Students have found areas of two-dimensional figures and volumes of prisms and cylinders. This lesson ends the unit.

Investigating Volume of Pyramids and Cones

Learn

Think about the difference between cones and pyramids.

The base of a pyramid has a polygonal shape. The base of a cone has a circular shape.

Find a cone and a cylinder that have the same height and radius. What fraction of the cylinder's volume is the cone's volume?

Fill the cone with water or sand and pour it into the cylinder. How many times does it take to fill the cylinder?

Get a basin of water. Put the cone under the water. Mark the water level. Do the same thing with the cylinder. Compare the water levels.

A pyramid has the same volume formula as a cone.

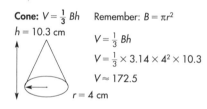

Cone: $V = \frac{1}{3} Bh$ Remember: $B = \pi r^2$

$h = 10.3$ cm

$V = \frac{1}{3} Bh$

$V = \frac{1}{3} \times 3.14 \times 4^2 \times 10.3$

$V \approx 172.5$

$r = 4$ cm

The volume of the cone is about 172.5 cm³.

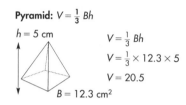

Pyramid: $V = \frac{1}{3} Bh$

$h = 5$ cm

$V = \frac{1}{3} Bh$

$V = \frac{1}{3} \times 12.3 \times 5$

$V = 20.5$

$B = 12.3$ cm²

The volume of the pyramid is 20.5 cm³.

Try

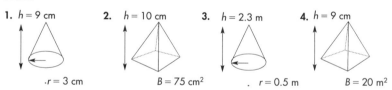

1. $h = 9$ cm

$r = 3$ cm

2. $h = 10$ cm

$B = 75$ cm²

3. $h = 2.3$ m

$r = 0.5$ m

4. $h = 9$ cm

$B = 20$ m²

NCTM Process Standards Analysis and Focus

The standards analysis examines how the process standards have been incorporated into the above lesson. By increasing the focus on three of the process standards, a more effective and meaningful lesson can be presented. The suggestions offered can help you to think about how this might be accomplished.

Connections The lesson suggests a connection between the volumes of a cone and a cylinder of the same radius and height.

Suggestion → Students already know how to find the volume of prisms and cylinders. Examine the relationships between prisms and pyramids and between cylinders and cones. Connecting those relationships with the formulas for the figures will help

Practice

Find the volume of each figure.

1.
   $r = 3$ m
   $h = 4$ m

2.
   $B = 24$ m^2
   $h = 8$ m

3.
   $r = 5.5$ cm
   $h = 7$ cm

4.
   $B = 72$ cm^2
   $h = 12$ cm

5. pyramid
   $B = 3.5$ dm^2
   $h = 0.9$ dm

6. cone
   $r = 4$ cm
   $h = 3$ cm

7. pyramid
   $B = 1,200$ cm^2
   $h = 15$ cm

8. pyramid
   $B = 2.7$ m^2
   $h = 0.4$m

9. cone
   $r = 12$ m
   $h = 10$ m

10. cone
    $r = 43$ mm
    $h = 50$ mm

11. pyramid
    $B = 6,232$ dm^2
    $h = 8.1$ dm

12. cone
    $r = 0.3$ km
    $h = 0.5$ km

13. Find the volume of a cone with a height of 12.4 cm and base with a radius of 6 cm.

14. Find the volume of a pyramid whose height is of 8.2 m and a square base whose edge lengths are 3 m.

Apply

15. A pyramid has a square base with each edge 5 m long. A cone has a diameter of 5 m. Both the cone and the pyramid are 6 m in height. What is the difference in m^3 between the two?

16. Which would weigh more, a cylinder of iron with a radius of 2 cm and 2 cm high or a cone with a radius of 3 cm and 2 cm high? Explain.

students see how mathematical ideas can become extensions of prior knowledge.

Representation Students find volumes using information from labeled drawings or from values representing the dimensions of cones or pyramids.

Suggestion → Reinforce the relationships between a prism and a pyramid and between a cone and a cylinder by having students sketch the related figures next to each other or one inside the other. If it is possible to provide geometric shapes for students to handle, this will help students compare the relative volumes and see the reasonableness of the formulas.

Reasoning and Proof The lesson suggests students pour sand from a cone into a cylinder of the same height and radius or submerge figures in water and gauge the amount of water displaced to find the volume relationships.

Suggestion → To help students gain greater insight into volume relationships, have them vary dimensions in the formulas and discuss the results. Demonstrate the hands-on comparisons suggested in the lesson, and help students understand that while the demonstrations approximate volume relationships, the accuracy of either method in a classroom situation is questionable and does not constitute proof.

Communication In the lesson development, communication is limited to answering direct questions. Opportunities to discuss relationships and clarify thinking about those relationships occur belatedly at the end of the lesson. Note that an increased focus on reasoning and proof will also lead to increased communication.

Problem Solving Exploring the relationship between the volumes of a cone and a pyramid is presented as a problem-solving activity without discussion of why the activity does not constitute a proof. Finding a dimension when given information about volume is not part of the lesson.

The teaching plan that follows shows how the suggestions for increasing the focus on the process standards can be implemented.

Revised Teaching Plan

Materials → A variety of three-dimensional models of prisms, pyramids, cylinders, and cones

BEGIN THE LESSON with a brief review of finding volume of prisms and cylinders. Have students determine the volume of a few figures, and then explain that there are other figures with the same base and height within prisms and cylinders. Draw a prism on the board and demonstrate how a pyramid can be formed within the figure. Have students make similar drawings at their desks. Do this for a variety of prisms, including cubes, rectangular prisms, triangular prisms, and pentagonal prisms. If possible, allow students to examine models of the figures. Repeat the activity with cones and cylinders by demonstrating how a cone fits inside a cylinder. Examining models and completing sketches will help students visualize the volume relationships.

How would the volume of a pyramid compare to the volume of a prism with the same base and height? (The volume of the pyramid would be less.) *Why?* (The pyramid does not take up all the space within the prism.) Ask a similar question involving cylinders and cones. You may wish to have students estimate the fraction of the volume of the prism/cylinder that is contained in the pyramid/cone.

EXPLAIN THAT THE FORMULA for the volume of a pyramid is related to the formula for the volume of a prism. In fact, the volume of a pyramid is $\frac{1}{3}$ the volume of a prism of equal height and base. Walk students through an example of this relationship. *Suppose a rectangular prism has square bases and its volume is 90 cubic cm. If a square pyramid has the same height and its base is equal to the prism's, what is the volume of the pyramid?* (30 cubic cm)

Now write the formulas for the prism ($V = Bh$) and the pyramid ($V = \frac{1}{3} Bh$) on the board. Have students compare the two formulas and explain them in words; that is, the volume of a pyramid with a given base and height is one-third the volume of a prism with the same base and height. Next, explain that there is a similar relationship between the formula for the volume of a cone and the formula for the volume of a cylinder. Write those two formulas and ask students to interpret their relationship in words. Connecting the verbal explanation to the symbolic representation will make the formulas more meaningful and help students remember them more readily.

At this point, you may wish to demonstrate the relationships by filling shapes with sand or having students observe the amount of water displaced when shapes are submerged in water. Emphasize that these activities help us think about the volume relationships but do not constitute mathematical proofs. Students should be able to articulate that there is much room for inaccuracy in measuring and reading results.

f.y.i.

The height of a pyramid or cylinder is the perpendicular distance between the vertex (highest point from the base) of the figure and its base.

What Might Happen . . . What to Do

Students may have difficulty identifying the height of the pyramid or cone. Frequently, the height is shown as a line drawn within the figure that extends perpendicularly from the center of the circle or face of the prism to the figure's vertex. Demonstrate this for students, but, help them understand that it is possible to have a lopsided (oblique) cone or pyramid in which the highest point is not over the center of the base. It may help students to visualize the figures as a stack of thin slices that get pushed to a side. This change in position of the height does not change the volume of the figure.

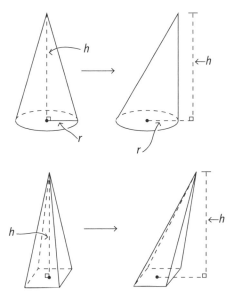

ENGAGE STUDENTS IN A DISCUSSION to help clarify their understanding of the volume relationships. *What would be the volume of a cone with the same height and base as a cylinder whose volume is 300 cubic centimeters?* (100 cubic centimeters) *If a cone has a volume of 40 cubic inches, what would be the volume of a cylinder with the same height and base? Explain how you found your answer.* (The volume of the cylinder is three times the volume of the cone; $3 \times 40 = 120$ cubic inches.) These questions enable students to recognize that if the volume of the cone is one third that of the related cylinder, then the volume of the related cylinder is three times that of the cone. *How can you find the height of a pyramid if you know the volume and area of the base?* (Divide volume by area of base and multiply by 3.) *Volume is expressed in cubic units. What type of unit represents the height?* (Linear units) The reasoning required to answer these questions will reinforce understanding of the volume relationships and will help students become better problem solvers.

CONCLUDE THE LESSON with questions that require students to think critically and help them gain a deeper understanding of the relationships represented in the formulas. Encourage students to explain how they arrive at their answers.

1. *Without computing, compare the volumes of a pyramid and a cone, each inscribed in a cube with edges measuring 5 feet.* (Since the area of the entire square is greater than the area of a circle inscribed in that square, the volume of the pyramid would be greater than the volume of the cone.)

2. *If you doubled the height of a cone and left the radius of its base unchanged, how would the volume be affected? How would doubling the diameter but not changing the height affect the volume?* (In each case the volume would double.)

3. *How would the volume of a cone be affected if both the height and radius were doubled?* (The volume would be four times as great.)

4. *If the sides of a square pyramid were doubled but the height was unchanged, how would the volume be affected? If the height were halved?* (Volume with unchanged height would be four times greater; with height halved, the volume would double.)

Extension

Encourage students to visualize a cone as the "last" figure in a sequence of pyramids with increasing numbers of shorter sides in the bases. This intuitively justifies that a pyramid and cone have the same volume formula.

Student Pages

Students are now ready to complete exercises similar to those on the reduced student pages. Suggest that students write the formula for each exercise and identify the value of each variable before calculating the volume.

Assessment

As students made drawings and participated in discussions, there were opportunities to assess their spatial visualization skills and understanding of the volume relationships. When students found the volumes of various pyramids and cones, it was possible to judge their abilities to choose the appropriate formula and carry out the computation.

NCTM Standards Summary

The lesson guided students in building on prior knowledge as they examined the relationships between prisms and pyramids and between cylinders and cones. Connecting those relationships with the formulas used to find the volumes of figures helped develop a keener understanding of volume relationships and made the formulas more reasonable and meaningful for students. Using the formulas as the basis for problem solving helped extend understanding of how to apply the relationships and provided a review of measurement units. The reasoning required to explain how volume is affected by changing dimensions of a figure helped students gain greater insight into the relationships among the variables that determine volume. Finally, the lesson afforded ample opportunities for students to communicate their ideas and understandings about volume relationships and computational methods.

Standard 5 **Data Analysis and Probability**

AT THE SEVENTH GRADE LEVEL, data analysis and probability includes a lot of work with different graphical representations of data, statistical representations of a set of data, and probability concepts. Our lessons are derived from these important topics, and include a lesson on using the measures of central tendency to represent a set of data, a lesson in which students have to interpret information from a graph that may be missing some information, a lesson that focuses on the differences between theoretical and experimental probabilities, and a lesson on interpreting a circle graph.

Three lessons model how the process standards can be used to teach content. A fourth lesson is a hypothetical textbook lesson that we have revised to be more standards based. These four lessons do not represent the entire curriculum, but rather provide glimpses of how, with a more concentrated effort to incorporate the process standards, better mathematics teaching and learning can be achieved.

In one lesson we have chosen, students use the measures of central tendency to analyze a set of data. Using the process standards of problem solving, reasoning and proof, and communication, students not only must calculate the mean, median, and mode, but they also have to decide which measure best represents the set of data.

Another lesson we have chosen has students interpret graphical representations of data when some of the usual information is missing. By incorporating the process standards of representation, communication, and problem solving into the lesson, students reconstruct the story that might have resulted in the given graphical representation.

A third lesson that we have chosen is one that focuses students on the differences between theoretical and experimental probability. Through the process standards of communication, reasoning and proof, and connections, students conduct probability experiments, collecting data that translates to experimental probability. They come to realize that by increasing the number of trials, they move closer to matching the theoretical probability.

The hypothetical textbook lesson that we have chosen to revise is one in which students read and interpret information from a circle graph. Through better incorporation of the process standards of representation, communication, and connections, students are provided a more in-depth discussion of circle graphs, finding out more about how they are made and when they are most useful for representing data.

Standard 5 Lessons

Using Measures of Central Tendency

Interpreting Graphs

Investigating Probability

Reading and Interpreting Circle Graphs

Using Measures of Central Tendency

Introduction

Objective → Students will be able to use measures of central tendency (mean, median, and mode) as tools to analyze real-world data.

Context → Students can find the mean, median, and mode. Students will go on to further differentiate the measures and make other statistics representations. In this lesson students will determine which measure is the best for representing data in a given situation.

NCTM Standards Focus

Understanding how people use data to communicate is very important in today's society. Often, however, students are just told how to find the measures of central tendency and directed when to use each one. In this standards-based lesson, students look at situations and determine which of these measures best communicates information in the given situation. Experiences like this one will prepare them both to express their own views and intelligently judge the views of others.

Reasoning and Proof Students interpret real-world data by referencing measures of central tendency. They apply reasoning skills to determine which measure or measures best represent(s) the data with respect to the context in which it is presented.

Communication Students see that the measure of central tendency they choose to use to represent data greatly affects the information they communicate. Throughout the lesson students communicate their reasoning both orally and in writing.

Teaching Plan

Materials → Student pages 126–127

BEGIN THE LESSON by conducting a quick review of mean, median, and mode and how to determine them. Ask students to talk about times they have seen or used averages. Most of the time students have probably heard the mean reported. Ask them to think of times when the median or mode may have been a useful piece of information to report or know.

You may want to take a few minutes to point out to students that these measures are referred to as *measures of central tendency* and discuss the term with them. Tell students that today the focus of the lesson will be not just on finding the mean, median, and mode, but on determining which measure might be the best one to convey information about a particular situation.

Give each student a copy of student page 126. Because it may be helpful for students to discuss various ideas, you may wish to have them work with a partner or in groups. Review the problem situations with students to make sure they understand them. Tell them to find the mean, median, and mode for each set of data and then decide which of those measures would be the best one to describe the information. They also need to state why they chose a particular measure.

As students work in their groups you may wish to ask them some of these questions or give them these suggestions to help them reach a decision.

- *How do the measures of central tendency compare with each other?*
- *If you looked at a measure by itself, would it give you a good picture of what happened? Why or why not?*
- *Are there any "outliers" or pieces of data that don't follow the pattern of the rest of the data? How do these affect each measure of central tendency?*

One technique that might help students focus on the advantages and limitations of using a particular measure is to have members of the groups take a different measure of central tendency and try to convince the group that theirs is the best one to communicate the information. If the group agrees that this particular measure does not do a good job of describing the information they can take it out of consideration. This method of reasoning will help students not only in this exercise but also in looking at other situations.

Once students are finished, assemble them to present their opinions and their reasons for them. You may wish to ask what each group decided and have that group try to convince the class that their decision is the best one. While it may be difficult for a class to reach consensus, take the time to try for it. Striving for consensus will help students develop communication and their reasoning skills.

f.y.i.

An interesting point for students to note is that if there is a *mode,* it is actually part of the data set, while the *mean* and *median* may or may not be in the data set.

f.y.i.

Encourage students to reach consensus rather than vote in their groups to make decisions about which measure of central tendency to use. This will help students develop their reasoning skills as they try to understand and respond to other opinions and reasoning.

In the first problem, one of the important points is to make sure students understand what they are being asked to do. Some may think that since the player has been stealing a lot of bases lately, they are to tell about his recent stolen base productivity. The question is to tell about his stolen base productivity over his career. The mean would be a logical choice and is often used in sports averages. It reflects both the more productive and less productive years. The median would give you the midpoint of his stolen bases. In this case it is also a fair representation of his productivity. Because he had some very lean years and some very good years, the median is in line with the mean. The mode, while close to the mean and median, is not as meaningful, since it really represents only two of the eleven data points.

In the second problem, the median is probably the best indicator. The mean is skewed slightly by the low score of 25. The mode is not meaningful because there are so many different data points.

To conclude the lesson, present the following problem.

> The hourly salaries for the workers at a fast food restaurant are $5.50, $6.00, 6.50, $7.00, $8.00, $10.00, $24.00, and $25.00. What are the mean, median, and mode of the salaries? If you were a worker, what would you say the average salary is? If you were the owner and wanted to get someone to come to work for you, what would you say the average salary is?

The mean is $11.50; the median is $7.50; there is no mode. The worker may say the average salary is the median because it more closely reflects what 75% of the people get paid. The owner might say the mean since it is the highest measure of central tendency. While students may disagree, this is an interesting problem because there are obviously two types of workers here. (A reasonable guess is that one salary is for the workers and the other is for the managers.) The $7.50 is in the middle of the cluster of the workers. The mean of $11.50 represents no one but is somewhere between the higher paid employees and the lower paid ones.

Student Pages

Student page 126 provides problems for use during the lesson. Student page 127 provides similar problems for homework.

Assessment

You had the opportunity to assess students in their groups as they solved problems and discussed which measure of central tendency to use. You were able to further assess students' understanding and reasoning as students presented their solutions and arguments.

NCTM Standards Summary

In this lesson, students applied reasoning skills to determine which measure or measures of central tendency best represented the data for a given situation. In all cases, students used communication skills to explain and defend their reasoning.

Answers

Page 126
1. Mean: 30.55; Median: 33;
   Mode: 36. See lesson discussion.
2. Mean: 85.36; Median: 88;
   Mode: 78 and 94. See lesson
   discussion.

Page 127
1. Mean: 71.47; Median: 72;
   Mode: 72. Answers will vary.
2. Mean: $192,000; Median:
   $131,000; Mode: none. Answers
   will vary.
3. Player A: Mean: 12.55;
   Median: 12; Mode: 14
   Player B: Mean: 12.73;
   Median: 16; Mode: 6
   Answers will vary.

Using Measures of Central Tendency

Find the mean, median, and mode. Then answer the questions.

❶ The table shows the number of bases stolen by one baseball player for the years 1989–1999. Which measure or measures would you use to best describe the player's number of stolen bases per year over his career? Explain your reasoning.

Year	Stolen Bases
1989	4
1990	15
1991	10
1992	8
1993	33
1994	25
1995	36
1996	40
1997	36
1998	66
1999	63

❷ Students in Mrs. Rivera's math class at Jefferson Middle School recorded the following scores on their last test. Which measure or measures would you use to best describe how the class performed on this test? Explain your reasoning.

78, 94, 83, 78, 100,
85, 92, 94, 70, 84,
94, 98, 78, 25, 97,
86, 93, 91, 88, 79,
93, 82, 87, 95, 90

Standard 5 Data Analysis and Probability

Using Measures of Central Tendency

**Find the mean, median, and mode for each data set.
Then answer the questions.**

1 The following high temperatures were recorded in San Diego, California for the first 15 days of January. Which measure or measures would you use to best describe the temperature in San Diego during this time? Explain your reasoning.

72°, 72°, 70°, 64°, 66°,
72°, 78°, 78°, 80°, 72°,
70°, 72°, 66°, 68°, 72°

2 Beckman Realty sold 12 houses last quarter. Listed are the selling prices for each of the houses they sold. Which measure or measures would you use to describe the average cost of a home that Beckman Realty sold last quarter? Explain your reasoning.

$85,000	$156,000	$124,000
$350,000	$98,000	$259,000
$128,000	$127,000	$298,000
$116,000	$429,000	$134,000

3 Imagine you have an opening on your school basketball team. Two new players are vying for the opening. Below are their point totals for the 11 games played last season with their previous teams. Which player would you select for the team? Refer to the measures for each player to support your selection.

Player A: 14, 12, 11, 9, 12, 10, 15, 14, 11, 16, 14

Player B: 6, 17, 7, 22, 3, 16, 6, 21, 18, 5, 19

Interpreting Graphs

Introduction

Objective → Students will be able to interpret and construct graphical representations of data.

Context → Students have worked with all types of graphs. This lesson comes at the end of a section on graphing. Students will need a good sense of graphing since they will be working with less information than they may be used to.

NCTM Standards Focus

The standards call for students to be able to interpret graphical representations of data. By working with a graph that does not contain a title or labels and values, students are forced to look at the critical attributes of the graph in order to make sense of the story the graph is telling. In this standards-based lesson, students learn to carefully analyze the physical representation of graphs, enabling them to tell stories that accurately reflect the data being displayed on the graphs.

Representation Students focus on representations that are missing information. They need to make generalizations about this information in order to put a story to the information that could reflect what the representation is saying.

Communication Students look at the essence of communication as they try to interpret the trends a graph is showing and then piece together a story that could possibly have been used to generate the data shown on the graph.

Problem Solving Students look at problem-solving in a somewhat different way, as they begin with a picture of a situation and then attempt to determine what the original situation could have been.

Teaching Plan

Materials → Student pages 132–133; grid paper

BEGIN THE LESSON by having students share different types of graphs they are familiar with. As they share, ask them to list the important characteristics of the graphs. Expect to hear responses like: titles, appropriate labels, values, etc. *Does a graph really need to have these things to effectively tell a story?* Allow students to share their responses. It is important for students to understand that a graph's main goal is to communicate information, which, in effect, is to tell some kind of story.

Tell students that for today's lesson, they are going to be given a line graph that has no information other than the line itself and the markings on the x- and y-axes. There is no scale for either axis. Tell them that it is their task to determine what information or story the graph could be telling.

ARRANGE STUDENTS IN GROUPS of 3–4. Pass out a copy of student page 132 to each student. Ask students to tell what information the graph is communicating. Students may respond that the graph is telling them that something, perhaps price or speed, is increasing.

When you have exhausted the discussion about what information students can glean from the graph, focus the discussion on what information the graph does not provide. Students may notice the graph lacks a title, a scale for each axis, and the information about what each axis is measuring.

DIRECT STUDENTS' ATTENTION to the instructions below the graph. Ask what they notice about steps 2 and 3. Students should see that they are instructed to label the *time* and *distance* intervals that are appropriate for their story. *Which axis should be labeled* "time?" *Which should be labeled* "distance?" *Does it matter? How would the labels affect the story behind the graph?* Encourage students to think about these questions, but do not ask for responses at this time.

Tell students to work in their groups to complete student page 132. Tell them that their "stories" should give an overall picture of what might have happened, as well as tell what happened at each section of the line graph. The goal is to find a plausible explanation for the graph; there is no one correct answer. A correct answer is one that fits the information on the graph. Alternately, you may wish to let students have this discussion in their groups.

What Might Happen . . . What to Do

Students may have trouble getting started. If that is the case, you may want to take a minute and have students describe what is happening in each section of the line. For example, the line shows an increase, then a period of no increase, then a longer increase at a rate similar to the initial one, then a very slow increase, and finally an increase not as steep as earlier ones, but not as slow as the last one. If some groups are still having difficulty, consider giving them "what if " ideas, such as "What if the graph is telling a story about a trip?" What could be happening?

While students are working, circulate among the groups and pose questions that force them to think about the choices they have made. Possible questions could include:

- *Why did you place* Time *along the x-axis? the y-axis?*
- *Why did you place* Distance *along the x-axis? the y-axis?*
- *How would your story be affected if you reversed the labels?*
- *What can you infer occurred between the 2nd and 3rd intervals along the x-axis? How could this help you to determine where to place your labels?*

If necessary, help students see that if time were on the *y*-axis, then someone would travel a certain distance in no time (when the line is horizontal).

Once students have completed student page 132, bring them back together as a whole class. Have each group give a brief presentation of their completed graph and have the group tell the story that their graph could describe. Encourage those listening to ask clarifying questions or point out any discrepancies in the group's story as it relates to the graph. This active communication will result in significant critical thinking that will ultimately benefit all students.

While students are sharing their graphs, make sure they back up their stories with the information on the graph. If they don't, have other students challenge the stories or challenge them yourself. You also may want to intersperse the following questions to help students think about time and distance graphs in general.

- *How might we interpret distance? Is it how far we are from the starting point or is it the total distance traveled?*
- *What can we say about rate as a product of the relationship between time and distance? What does "fast" look like? What does "slow" look like?*
- *What is implied when there is no change between intervals?*

There are many possible explanations for this graph. For example, almost any mode of transportation can work. What students need to see is that the trip is started and a rate of speed is reached after an initial warm-up period. Then the trip stops for a period of time. The trip picks back up and then something, such as a hill or sight-seeing slows the trip down. Finally the pace picks back up. Other explanations are possible.

You may wish to assign page 133 for homework to end the lesson.

Student Pages

Student worksheet page 132 is the graph for the class. Student page 133 presents a task similar to the one completed in class.

Assessment

While students worked in groups, you assessed their ability to interpret a graph that lacked critical information. You observed as students worked to make sense of the graph and constructed a story or list of events that reflected the information in the graph. During group presentations, you observed and assessed students' thought processes through the critical thinking questions posed. You also assessed student's understanding as they individually completed a task similar to the group task.

NCTM Standards Summary

In this lesson students focused on using reasoning skills as they analyzed a graph that was lacking information. Students made generalizations about what information the graph was communicating and used this information to tell a plausible story that fit the information that they had. In addition, students constructed their own individual graph and story, reinforcing what they had learned through the small group task. Throughout this lesson, students communicated their thinking and understanding both through group and whole class discussion and through their writing.

Answers

Page 132
Answers may vary. See lesson for possible answers.

Page 133
Answers may vary

Interpreting Graphs

Use the graph to answer the questions.

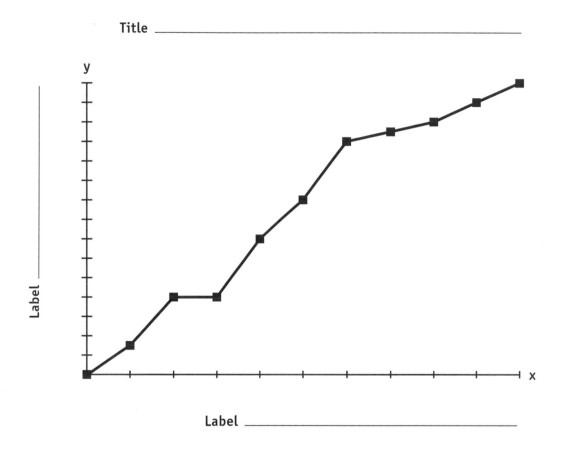

Title _____

Label (y-axis)

Label (x-axis)

① Work with your group to create a story that this graph might represent. Be sure to describe specifically what is happening and how the graph backs up your story.

② Use one axis to show time and the other to show distance.

③ Mark the distance and time intervals that are appropriate for your story.

④ Choose an appropriate title for your story and graph.

Standard 5 Data Analysis and Probability

Interpreting Graphs

Complete the following.

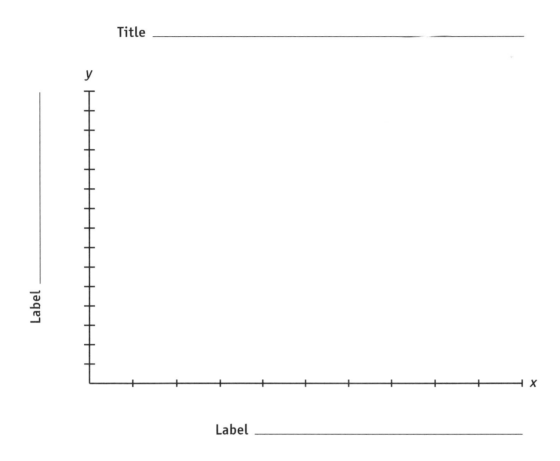

Title _____

① Create your own story that can be represented graphically. Be sure to describe specifically what is happening and how the graph supports your story.

② Label each axis and name the intervals on each axis.

③ Draw the graph.

④ Choose an appropriate title for your story and graph.

Investigating Probability

Introduction

Objective → Students will describe the difference between theoretical and experimental probability.

Context → This lesson comes midway in a unit about ratio, percent, and probability. Students have learned basic probability concepts and have determined probabilities for single events. They will go on to work with compound events, counting techniques, simulations, and predictions.

NCTM Standards Focus

In this standards-based lesson, students will be actively engaged in gathering data and comparing outcomes to those for theoretical probability. Through their own reasoning processes, students will come to recognize that the larger the number of trials, the more closely experimental probability approaches theoretical probability. As they communicate their ideas, students will clarify the difference between the two types of probability and gain insight into making predictions. Connections will be made between ratios and percents and probability as students solve application problems. Emphasizing the connection experimental probability has to real-world situations makes the concept more meaningful and interesting for the students.

Communication Students report the data results of experiments they conduct and discuss the reasons for the differences between theoretical and experimental probability.

Reasoning and Proof Students analyze a variety of situations to determine theoretical probability and compare the results with outcomes of activities in which they gather data. This highlights the difference between theoretical and experimental probability. By combining their data, students gain insight into the fact that the gap between experimental and theoretical probability decreases as the number of experimental trials is increased.

Connections As students find the probability of outcomes, they draw on their knowledge of ratios, decimals, and percents. Connections to real-world situations illustrate how experimental probabilities are used and help students recognize probability as the basis for predictions made regarding politics, sports, weather, and so on.

Teaching Plan

Materials → Student pages 138–139; number cubes; spinners; counters; coins; bottle caps

BEGIN THE LESSON by having students examine several situations in which they can determine the theoretical probability that an event will occur. This will also serve to review the fundamental concept that probability is a measure of chance that allows us to predict the likelihood of an event.

- *When you flip a fair coin, how many outcomes are possible?* (2) *What can you say about the likelihood of those outcomes?* (They are equally likely.) *If you flip the coin once, what is the probability that heads will occur?* ($\frac{1}{2}$) *How do you know?* (The ratio of favorable outcomes to possible outcomes is 1 to 2.)

- *If you use a spinner that is equally divided into fourths that are shaded red, green, blue, and yellow, what is the probability of the spinner landing on green with one spin? Explain.* ($\frac{1}{4}$; There are four likely outcomes, of which green is one of them.) *If you spin 40 times, how many times would you expect to spin red? Why?* ($P(\text{red}) = \frac{1}{4}$; $\frac{1}{4}$ of 40 = 10)

- *If you use a fair number cube, what is the probability of rolling a 3 on any one roll?* ($\frac{1}{6}$) *If you rolled the number cube 60 times, how many times would you expect to roll 3? Why?* (10; $\frac{1}{6}$ of 60 = 10)

Tell students that they are going to conduct an experiment with the number cube. Have them work in pairs. Tell them to take turns rolling the number cube and keeping a tally of the results. Instruct them to complete a total of 60 rolls and make a table to record their results.

Number on Cube	1	2	3	4	5	6
Tally						
Total						
Experimental Probability						

WHEN ALL GROUPS HAVE completed the experiment, have groups report their results. *How many times did the number 3 actually appear? What was the experimental probability of rolling 3?* Have groups compare their values for $P(3)$ and for each of the other numbers. You might suggest that students create a double-bar graph to compare the predicted appearances for each number to the experimental results.

ASK STUDENTS TO OFFER any ideas they have about why the experimental and theoretical probabilities differ. Be sure students understand that experimental results do not change the theoretical probabilities—theoretical probabilities are "ideal," or expected values, which may or may not be reproduced by the results of an experiment.

What effect would increasing the number of trials have on the experimental probability? (Experimental probability would come closer to theoretical

f.y.i.

The *experimental probability* is the probability based on the results or data acquired from conducting an experiment. It is the ratio of favorable outcomes to total outcomes in the experiment.

© Creative Publications

f.y.i.

In many real-life situations, experimental probability may be the only way to assign a probability to an event. Experimental probabilities are very common in sports and business situations. For example, a basketball player's likelihood of making his or her next free throw is based on an experimental probability. Life insurance premiums are based on the probability that a person will live to a certain age, and car insurance premiums are based on the probability that a person will be involved in an accident or have their car stolen. All of these probabilities are developed using data that has been collected from a large number of cases.

probability.) Explore this idea by combining each group's results into class results. Create a table on the board to record the combined totals for all of the groups. *Are the experimental probabilities different now? How do they compare to the theoretical probabilities? What do you think might happen if you could toss the number cube 6 million or 600 million times?* (Experimental probabilities will get closer and closer to theoretical probabilities.) It is interesting to note that when the number of trials is large and experimental probabilities do not reflect theoretical probabilities, there may be reason to suspect that the theoretical model does not fit the situation—as would happen if, for example, a coin or number cube was biased. As students discuss these issues, both the difference and the link between experimental and theoretical probability will become clearer.

CONCLUDE THE LESSON by presenting additional situations for students to consider.

- *A basketball player has made 40 out of 65 free throws. Based on this data, what is the probability that she will make her next free throw?* ($\frac{8}{13}$ or 61.5%) *About how many of her next 40 free throw attempts would you predict she will make? Explain.* (25; 61.5% of 40 is 24.6)

- *Experience has shown that 1,000 out of 500,000 microchips manufactured by a company are defective. Based on this evidence, what is the probability that a chip picked at random from the company's assembly line will be defective?* ($\frac{1}{500}$ or 0.2%) *Do you think this is reliable information? Why?* (Yes; the number of chips examined was quite large.)

If time allows, encourage students to suggest other real-world situations that involve experimental probability. Have the class indicate whether they agree that each example reflects experimental probability, whether they think theoretical probability is being used, and have them explain their thinking.

Extension

Pair students to play a game based on experimental probability. Provide pairs with a spinner that is divided into 12 equal regions and instruct students to shade 4 of the regions red, 3 blue, 3 green, and 2 yellow. Give each pair 12 counters.

Tell students to determine the theoretical probability of spinning each color. Instruct students to decide how to distribute their counters on the colors, keeping in mind that a counter should be removed when the spinner lands on any section of the color it is placed on. The object of the game is to clear the spinner of all counters. The first player to clear his/her spinner wins.

After they play the game, hold a discussion in which students explain how they used theoretical probability to decide where to place the counters.

Student Pages

Student page 138 provides additional experiments in which students can compare probabilities and compare experimental and theoretical values. Page 139 provides practice exercises involving data.

Assessment

As students responded during discussions at the beginning of the lesson, it was possible to assess their understanding of theoretical probability. Their completed data tables served as indicators of students' proficiency in carrying out an experiment and determining the related probabilities. Finally, during the follow-up discussion, it was possible to evaluate students' grasp of experimental probability concepts.

NCTM Standards Summary

Students gathered and analyzed data and they compared actual (experimental) results to expected (theoretical) results. Activating their own reasoning processes enabled students to recognize that the larger the number of trials, the more closely experimental probability approaches theoretical probability. Communicating their ideas helped students to clarify the difference between the two types of probability and gain insight into making predictions. Students connected their knowledge about ratios and percents to probability as they solved application problems. Emphasizing the connection between experimental probability and real-world situations made the concept more meaningful and interesting for the students.

Answers

Page 138

1. Theoretical probabilities are $\frac{1}{2}$; experimental probabilities will vary.

2. Theoretical probabilities are $\frac{1}{2}$; experimental probabilities will vary.

3. Answers will vary.

4. Answers will vary.

Page 139

1. $\frac{1}{5}$
2. $\frac{4}{25}$
3. $\frac{7}{50}$
4. $\frac{11}{50}$
5. $\frac{9}{50}$
6. $\frac{1}{10}$
7. $\frac{13}{25}$
8. $\frac{12}{25}$
9. $\frac{21}{100}$
10. $\frac{19}{50}$
11. $\frac{13}{50}$
12. $\frac{3}{20}$
13. $\frac{47}{100}$
14. 0
15. No; you may not have picked an orange marble even if there were one or more. However, it is unlikely that there was an orange marble.
16. 65
17. $\frac{3}{10}$
18. 0.003 or 0.3%
19. 4 days
20. The coin is not fair; 10,000 is a large number and the number of heads should be closer to 5000 with a fair coin.

Investigating Probability

Work with a partner.

❶ Flip a coin 10 times and record your results in the table. Then calculate the theoretical and experimental probability for this experiment.

Coin Experiment #1

Heads	Tails

Theoretical Probability

P(heads) _____

P(tails) _____

Experimental Probability

P(heads) _____

P(tails) _____

❷ Flip the coin 100 times and record your results in the table. Then calculate the theoretical and experimental probability for this experiment.

Coin Experiment #2

Heads	Tails

Theoretical Probability

P(heads) _____

P(tails) _____

Experimental Probability

P(heads) _____

P(tails) _____

❸ Compare your results in 1 and 2. How did the experimental and theoretical values compare in each case? If the results were different, give a reason why you think this is so. Which results would you consider more reliable?

❹ Work with a partner. Toss a bottle cap 100 times and record the number of times it lands "up" and the number of times it lands "down" in the table. Then calculate the theoretical and experimental probability for this experiment.

Bottle Cap Experiment

Up	Down

Theoretical Probability

P(up) _____

P(down) _____

Experimental Probability

P(up) _____

P(down) _____

Do you think "landing up" and "landing down" are equally likely events? Explain. Based on your experimental results, how many times would you expect the cap to land "up" in 1000 tosses? To land "down"?

Investigating Probability

Use the table to find each experimental probability.

Results of a number cube being tossed 50 times.

Number on Cube	1	2	3	4	5	6
Number of Outcomes	10	8	7	11	9	5

❶ P(1)_____

❷ P(2) _____

❸ P(3)_____

❹ P(4)_____

❺ P(5)_____

❻ P(6) _____

❼ P(odd number)_____

❽ P(even number)_____

The table shows the results of an experiment in which one marble was selected from a box, its color recorded, and the marble was returned to the box before the next selection. Find each experimental probability.

Color	Times Selected
Red	21
Blue	38
Green	26
Yellow	15

❾ P(red)_____

❿ P(blue)_____

⓫ P(green)_____

⓬ P(yellow)_____

⓭ P(red or green)_____

⓮ P(orange)_____

⓯ Can you conclude that there are no orange marbles in the box? Explain your answer. **Solve each problem.**

⓰ In the next 250 picks, how many times would you expect to get a green marble?

⓱ Roger shot 20 arrows and hit the bull's eye 14 times. Find the experimental probability that on his next shot Roger will not hit the bull's eye.

⓲ On a production line, 12 defective CD players were found among 4000 randomly selected players. What is the probability of a CD player being defective?

⓳ Records show that there are 9 rainy days in Houston during the month of January. Sharon is planning a two-week trip to Houston next January. About how many rainy days should she expect?

⓴ Suppose you toss a coin 10,000 times. Heads come up 983 times and tails come up the other times. What might you conclude about the coin? Explain.

Reading and Interpreting Circle Graphs

Introduction

Objective → Students will read and interpret circle graphs.

Context → This lesson appears early in a unit on data analysis in which students have already studied line graphs. They will go on to work with scattergrams and measures of central tendency.

Reading and Interpreting Circle Graphs

Learn

A circle graph shows how parts of something relate to a whole.

These circle graphs show you the proportion of people in different age groups in Asia and South America in 1999.

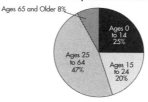

Asia's Population 3.5 Billion

South America's Population 530 Million

Talk

In 1999 the world's population reached 6 billion people.

1. How many people lived in Asia?

2. What is the sum of the percentages in each circle?

You can use these benchmarks to estimate the size of a section of a circle graph, or the number each part represents.

$$50\% = \frac{1}{2} \qquad 25\% = \frac{1}{4} \qquad 33\% = \frac{1}{3} \qquad 10\% = \frac{1}{10}$$

How many people in Asia were between the ages of 25 and 64?

47% is a little less than $\frac{1}{2}$, and $\frac{1}{2}$ of 3.5 billion is 1.75 billion.

So, about 1.75 billion people in Asia were between the ages of 25 and 64.

Try

1. How many people in Asia were 65 years and older?

2. How many people in South America were between the ages of 0 and 24?

NCTM Process Standards Analysis and Focus

The standards analysis examines how the process standards have been incorporated into the above lesson. By increasing the focus on three of the process standards, a more effective and meaningful lesson can be presented. The suggestions offered can help you to think about how this might be accomplished.

Representation Student pages show circle graphs with sections labeled in percents to indicate amounts represented.

Suggestion → **Compare different graphs of the same information to show the advantage circle graphs offer for representing certain types of data. Help students determine how sections represented in a circle graph relate to each other and the whole. This approach**

© Creative Publications

Practice

This graph compares the population in different parts of the world.

World Population: 6 Billion
Africa 12%
Europe 11%
South America 11%
North America 8%
Asia 58%

Use the circle graph to answer these questions.

1. By what percentage does the population of Europe outnumber the population of North America?

2. Does more or less than half of the world's population live in Asia?

3. Does more or less than one tenth of the world's population live in South America?

4. Out of 1,000 people, how many would you expect to live in Africa?

5. Out of 50 people, how many would you expect to live in North America?

Math Reasoning

Tell what is wrong with each circle graph.

6.
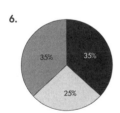
35% 35% 25%

7.
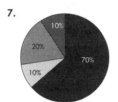
10% 20% 10% 70%

8.
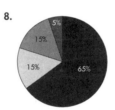
5% 15% 15% 65%

will help students decide when to choose a circle graph to represent data and clarify their understanding of how to interpret these graphs.

Communication Communication consists of answering direct questions about the graphs presented. Answers can be given as an individual activity in written form or orally; however, answers do not invite discussion.

Suggestion → Increase the focus on why and how circle graphs are created. Doing so will open up communication as students discuss their thoughts and insights. By identifying the important features of these graphs, students will extend their knowledge about how circle graphs are constructed and will be able to determine whether graphs are inaccurate or deceptive.

Connections Connections are made between sections of circle graphs and the information the sections represent. An important connection is made between the portion of the data represented as a fraction or percent and the size of the section of the circle.

Suggestion → Increase the attention given to connections between raw data, fractions, percentages, and circle graph measurement and how that information relates to constructing graphs. Through these connections, students will become aware of how various aspects of mathematics come together to create useful new ideas.

Problem Solving Interpreting graphs requires reasoning but does not involve problem solving.

Reasoning and Proof The lesson poses questions that call for interpreting data and require some reasoning to answer. Students are asked to think critically about incorrect graphs.

The teaching plan that follows shows how the suggestions for increasing the
focus on the process standards can be implemented.

Revised Teaching Plan

Materials → Overhead transparencies of various graphs

BEGIN THE LESSON by having students examine the same information presented as raw data, as a circle graph, and as a bar graph. Use
a circle graph from your own text pages, and ask students to display the
information in table form and to sketch a bar graph, or, use the information
presented here.

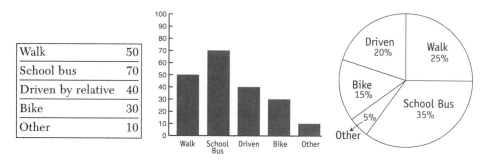

Walk	50
School bus	70
Driven by relative	40
Bike	30
Other	10

Have students think about each display. *How are these three representations
alike?* (Each shows the same information about methods of transportation;
each enables you to decide which method is most popular.) *How are they
different?* (One contains information in a table, another shows the same
information using bars, and the third uses a divided circle and represents
the information with percentages.) Ask students to explain how to use the
bar graph to determine the number of students who walk to school. *Can you
get that same information by reading the circle graph?* (Yes, if you know the
total number of students.) *With which representation is it easiest to compare
walkers to the total number of students?* (Circle graph) *When you look at the
circle graph, what general comparisons can you make between walkers and
each of the other methods?* (The walkers are the second largest group. There
are fewer walkers than bus riders, but more students walk than get driven
or ride bikes.) This discussion will help students identify the similarities and
differences among the representations and get them to recognize the advantages of each type of display.

FOCUS ATTENTION ON THE TYPES of questions that can be
answered by reading circle graphs. *Using only the circle graph, can you tell*

whether more students walk or ride a bicycle? (Yes.) *Can you tell how many more?* (Not without knowing the total number of students.) *Can you tell which form of transportation is most popular?* (Yes.) *How?* (It is the largest section, and it shows the greatest percentage.) *Can you tell how many students are driven to school? Explain.* (No, you need to know the total number of students.) *Can you determine which two forms of transportation together have the same number of students as the bus? Explain.* (Yes. Being driven, 20%, plus biking, 15%, equals 35%, which is the same as the percentage for bus riders.)

EXTEND THIS THINKING by presenting pairs of situations and asking for which pair a circle graph is appropriate. One example might be comparing total rainfall in a year for five cities. (A circle graph is not appropriate because there is not a natural whole or 100%.) Another example might be comparing total rainfall for each season for one city. (Yes, a circle graph would be appropriate here because each section would represent part of the total for one city.) Additional examples might include the number of hours different radio stations play certain types of music such as hip-hop, R & B, rock, and jazz; the number of students in the class who prefer each type of music; and so on. (A circle graph is not appropriate for the radio stations because there is not a natural whole or 100%. However, a circle graph would be appropriate for the students since members of the same class are being compared.) Having students discuss the representations will clarify how they can make effective choices to display data.

The construction of circle graphs is a somewhat involved procedure. However, these graphs are frequently used because they lend themselves to quick visual interpretation of the relationships among the fractional parts of a set of data as well as between each part and the data as a whole. You may wish to have students describe some circle graphs they have seen in magazines or newspapers. For example, government or corporate revenues and expenditures are often shown with a circle graph.

HOLD A BRIEF DISCUSSION on the procedure for creating a circle graph. Explain that a common method is to first express each piece of data as a fraction, then change each fraction to a percent, and finally, multiply the result by 360°, the number of degrees in a circle. Determining the sector of the circle to represent students that walk to school, for example, would be students walking ÷ total students = $\frac{50}{200} = \frac{1}{4}$; $\frac{1}{4}$ = 25%; and 25% × 360° = 90°. The final product equals the number of degrees that represent the percent and the fraction. A protractor would then be used to create a central angle for the circle with the correct number of degrees.

Have students help you work through the computation for the other forms of transportation to verify how the fractional parts, the percentages, and the number of degrees all equal the whole. In the case of the fractional parts, the sum is 1; for the percents, the sum is 100%; and for the degrees, the sum is 360°. Ask students why it was necessary to include the category "other." (Without it, the sum of the students would not equal 200 and the sum of the parts would not equal 1.) Tell students that when they are creating their own circle graphs they should draw the circles large enough so that the parts can be conveniently labeled.

Seize this opportunity to mention that, like all graphs, circle graphs can be constructed in such a way as to be deceptive. Advise students to examine circle graphs they encounter to determine whether the fractional parts total 1 or the percentages total 100%. Suggest, too, that they also visually check that the sections are accurately drawn. For example, a section labeled 25% would not and should not be equal to $\frac{1}{3}$ of the circle. Careful inspection of graphs will help to ascertain whether the graphical information seems reasonable and therefore reliable.

Assist students in making comparisons of sections within a circle graph by relating fractions to percentages of a circle. Connect to prior knowledge by drawing a circle and shading $\frac{1}{2}$, then asking students to name the shaded portion as a fraction and as a percent. You might also indicate the number of degrees that correspond, in this case, 180°. Do the same for $\frac{1}{4}$ of a circle and $\frac{1}{3}$ of a circle. Ask students how they would go about judging $\frac{1}{8}$ of a circle. Relating these measures to one another and to the portions of the circle they represent will help students make quick estimates of graph sections and help them interpret data more easily.

INSTRUCT STUDENTS TO DRAW a circle and divide it by estimating sections for percentages such as 30%, 15%, 45%, and 80%. Ask them to compare their estimates with a partner. Then invite volunteers to explain how they used certain benchmarks (like 50%) to decide on the size of each section. *What percent would correspond to $\frac{3}{4}$ of a circle?* (75%)

CONCLUDE THE LESSON by presenting a circle graph, such as the one below, which shows names for the data but not percentages. Have students estimate the percentages for each section. (Percentages are Taxes, 22%; Food, 25%; Clothing, 16%; Entertainment, 3%; Transportation, 6%; and Housing, 22%.) Ask questions that involve comparisons among the sections of the graph to promote understanding of the types of conclusions that can be drawn from the visual relationships.

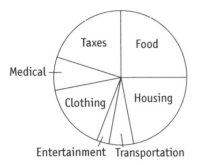

Student Pages

Students should be prepared to complete exercises similar to those on the reduced student pages.

Assessment

As students responded to questions during class discussions, you could assess their ability to read and interpret circle graphs. Students' circle drawings indicated their understanding of the relationship between percents and sections of the graph, as well as their general number sense.

NCTM Standards Summary

Increased class discussion afforded students the opportunity to explore how the sections of the circle relate to one another and to the whole. It also created awareness of how circle graphs can be used as an effective tool for analyzing data and making predictions. Emphasizing connections between raw data, fractions, percentages, and the sections of a circle enabled students to develop a better understanding of how these mathematical relationships are applied in constructing circle graphs. As students examined various graphs, their interpretation skills and insights into the visual representation of data were sharpened. They became aware of the type of data for which circle graphs are useful and how to recognize graphs that might be inaccurate.

Create Your Own Lesson

THIS LAST CHAPTER IS DESIGNED TO HELP you develop your own lessons in which you can comfortably incorporate the NCTM standards with your teaching style. We start with a list of questions to help you focus on factors to consider as you begin to organize a standards-based lesson. Then we model the process used to create a lesson as you are walked through the thoughts and decisions one person used in developing a lesson.

The questions listed here are meant as a guide, a starting point; they are offered to get you thinking about how to develop your lesson, what material to cover, what steps to follow, what questions to ask. Hopefully, these questions will trigger additional ideas that you will add as you go along.

Write down the ideas that come to you as you read each question. There may be questions for which you don't have an immediate response, but don't worry; as you begin working on your lesson, ideas will come. Start by selecting the general content area. Think about the concept you want to develop. Then, narrow in on an objective for the lesson. Be specific and be realistic. What does meeting that objective mean? Is there a skill that students should be able to perform after completing the lesson? Are there questions they should be able to answer? How will you determine that the objective has been met?

Next, think about the process standards: Problem Solving, Reasoning and Proof, Communication, Connections, and Representation. What approach will be effective in helping students understand the concept? Try to envision how the lesson will flow, how it should begin, what activities and questions will be included, and how you will assess learning. Understand that there can be several ways to successfully teach any lesson. As you begin to design your lesson, new ideas will come and you will be able to refine your thinking.

© Creative Publications

Focusing Questions

1. What content standard is to be addressed? What concept within that standard is to be developed?

2. What information do the standards offer about this content?

3. What do students know about this content? What don't they know?

4. What is the specific objective of the lesson? What should students be able to do at the end of the lesson?

recognize	identify	define
review	compute	classify
compare	create	other

5. What kinds of questions should students be able to answer when they complete this lesson? What skill(s) should they be able to demonstrate?

6. What resources are available to develop this concept?

references	textual material
manipulatives	supplementary material
colleagues	student knowledge

7. What can realistically be accomplished in the time allowed?

8. Which activities and process standards can best help develop the key ideas?
   - using drawings, charts, diagrams (Representation)
   - focusing on symbols (Representation)
   - conducting small-group/large-group discussion (Communication)
   - having students gather and analyze data (Problem Solving)
   - thinking through relationships and explaining them (Reasoning and Proof and Communication)
   - finding ways to prove thinking and verify solutions (Reasoning and Proof)
   - extending/building on former knowledge (Connections)
   - integrating concept with another discipline (Connections)
   - relating math to its use in the real world (Connections)

9. What questions will focus thinking on the concept and help guide learning?

Developing the Lesson

I AM WORKING ON A LESSON that focuses on exponents, which is part of the Numbers and Operations standard. Looking at math materials for this subject shows that most seem to present it in the same fashion: quickly, jumping right to the exponential form with little explanation. Knowing the emphasis the standards place on solid conceptual understanding, I believe that this lesson should definitely have some activities or experiences that can give students a clear understanding of what an exponential pattern is, or when it might apply in the real world.

I expect that my students have had little prior work with exponents. If they have, I suspect it involved memorizing the exponential form and practicing with problem sets. We hear the phrase used, *the rate increased exponentially*, but I wonder how many of my students know what that really means

My objective for this lesson is to have students see that when numbers have exponents, they represent a pattern of repeated multiplication, and then connect that understanding with the correct way to use exponents. I want my students to see that exponents are helpful in representing numbers that are very large or very small, like the size of a galaxy or the width of an electron. Exponents help us to express these vast or minute quantities. I think that is exciting. Toward these ends, I will use a problem-solving approach. As the process standard Problem Solving encourages, I will use a realistic situation.

As the standards suggest, I want my students to explore and investigate first, so that they start to construct their own understanding of concepts. From there, they can use representation and communication to place their understanding into their own mental schema. Once the students have gained a general understanding of exponents, I want them to work further with these powerful numbers. In particular, I want them to solve a rich exponents problem and use reasoning and proof to show that their answer is correct.

I guess at this point I have a general idea of what this lesson will look like: I will present some real-world scenarios that introduce exponents and have the students do some investigating and looking for patterns. I will then ask students to come up with ways of representing and communicating their understanding of exponents, explain the formal method of writing them, and then apply the knowledge to another problem.

The question on my mind now is, *What real-world scenarios can I use to engage the students in this lesson?* My students recently were intrigued by a discussion in which we talked about the book *The Andromeda Strain*, the story of a deadly virus that comes to planet Earth. I think something about viruses can captivate them again.

I will make up this data for my students.

Virus A

Time (in hrs./mins.)	:00	:20	:40	1:00	1:20
Number	1	2	4	8	16

Virus B

Time (in hrs./mins.)	:00	:30	1:00	1:30	2:00
Number	1	3	9	27	81

I selected these numbers for several reasons. First, because the viruses replicate at nearly the same rate, requiring students are required to investigate deeply to problem solve. If there were an obvious and large disparity between the rates, it would be too easy to state which virus would become a danger first. Second, I needed to come up with patterns that were exponential in nature so students could start to understand exponents in general. Finally, these rates are close to actual virus reproduction rates.

Problem 1

The Centers for Disease Control have become aware of two separate virus outbreaks in the United States. Both viruses are rapidly reproducing and will become a serious health risk once they have replicated themselves one million times. Study the data to determine which virus will first become a danger to the general public. Be prepared to show your work and explain your method of solving this problem.

I will have students work in groups to solve this problem. They will be instructed to solve it in any fashion that works for them, but there must be agreement within the group on the answer.

Discussing Problem 1

Which virus will become a health hazard first? How long did it take for each to replicate itself one million times? If students solve this problem correctly, they should see that Virus A needed 6 hours and 40 minutes to become one million strong, while Virus B needed 6 hours and 30 minutes. I will ask volunteer groups to share their answers and convince the class that they are correct.

While there is only one right answer to this problem (Virus B will become dangerous first.), there are multiple ways of solving it. To help the class see a variety of solution methods I will ask, *How did you solve the problem? Did anyone solve this problem in a different way?* Seeing a variety of problem-solving techniques and thinking should expand each student's own repertoire of problem-solving skills.

How did you record your data? I will ask this question because I want the students to think about their methods of representing data and to see some alternative methods.

While problem 1 does not formally teach the students about exponents, it provides them with a model of an exponential pattern to investigate. Problem 2 will pick up on this and lead the class to more formal teachings about exponents.

Problem 2

Analyze the data you have developed from the virus problem. What patterns do you see? Represent and communicate these patterns in any way that works for you. Be prepared to explain your thinking to your classmates.

Discussing Problem 2

What patterns did you find? Students should see that Virus A doubles itself every 20 minutes, and Virus B triples itself every 30 minutes. Students that do not see the pattern may have computed incorrectly. *How did you represent the pattern?* I want students to practice representing the patterns they are observing; it is good for them to see that there are multiple ways of expressing the same mathematical idea.

To move the discussion forward, I will ask, *If the pattern for Virus A is to double itself, can you think of a way to show how 128 is the result of doubling?* If a student responds that 128 is 64 times 2, I will reply, *How did the virus get to 64?* I want to lead the class to see that 128 is the same as $2 \times 2 \times 2 \times 2 \times 2 \times 2 \times 2$; that it was the number 2 that was multiplied by itself seven times to get to 128. This gets to the heart of exponents. *Can you represent any of the other numbers in Virus A as 2 being multiplied by itself multiple times?* I will ask this to help the class see that this type of representation can be used for all of the numbers (except 1) in the Virus A data. They can say $8 = 2 \times 2 \times 2$, or you can say 16 is $2 \times 2 \times 2 \times 2$.

Then we will focus on Virus B. *Can you represent 243 in a similar way?* $(3 \times 3 \times 3 \times 3 \times 3)$ This is the bridge to formal representations of exponents. *What do all of these numbers in the pattern have in common?* (Each can be represented as one number multiplied by itself multiple times.) I will ask this in order to bring the class closer to a working idea of what an exponent is. *Can you think of another number that you can represent in this way? For example, how could you represent 125 using 5?* I want the class to apply this type of representation to numbers not part of the pattern, so I can see if they are building an understanding.

Before I move the lesson forward, I want to take an opportunity to let the power of exponents sink in. *We are talking about numbers that are multiplied by themselves a certain number of times, and so far we have started with one-digit numbers such as 2 and 7. What would happen if we multiplied 50 by itself two, three, four, or even ten times?* I am hoping students will see that this would be an enormous number, one that, because of the difficulty of writing it out, might make other means of representation preferable. *How would you like to have to write out that number? Would you prefer a more efficient means to express the number?* I want the class to think about how continuous multiplying of the same number can be represented in a simpler way: *Can you state $3 \times 3 \times 3 \times 3 \times 3$ in words? Is there a symbolic way of representing this? Can you do it using numbers only?* This should elicit a variety of responses. I am gently steering the class to see that the method that has been developed to write $3 \times 3 \times 3 \times 3 \times 3$ as 3^5 makes sense. I will have the students represent and communicate their ideas.

By this time, I believe I will have laid a solid conceptual foundation for exponents. Now would be a good time to present the formal way of writing them. The words *base* and *exponent* will be defined and explained, and I will show various examples. Since the whole lesson has focused on repeated multiplication, I believe that 5^4, for example, will register in their minds as $5 \times 5 \times 5 \times 5$ rather than 5×4. I will lead the class through some sample problems with using exponents such as 6^3. We will go back to the earlier virus problems and record the number of virus replications using exponents. *Look at your data for Virus A. After four hours there were 4,096 replications of Virus A. Can you express this number using exponents?* (2^{12}). This question lets the students practice proper exponential form with numbers they have just worked with, hopefully helping them make the connection between the two different ways of representing the same number.

Reviewing the Plan

Before I teach this lesson, I'll review it again to make sure it is set up to meet my goals and utilize the standards effectively. I think that by having students analyze numbers and patterns, this lesson brings out the core idea of what exponential form means. I've built in a lot of opportunities for students to represent and communicate their thinking, and placed the lesson in a real-world context that I think they'll will find interesting.